# Television receivers

# Television receivers

**K.F. Ibrahim**

Senior Lecturer, Willesden College of Technology

Longman
Scientific &
Technical

**Longman Scientific & Technical,**
Longman Group UK Limited,
Longman House, Burnt Mill, Harlow,
Essex, CM20 2JE, England
*and Associated Companies throughout the world.*

First published 1992

ISBN 0 582 086175

**British Library Cataloguing in Publication Data**
A catalogue record for this book is available from
the British Library

Set by 4 in 10/12 pt Compugraphic Times.

Produced by Longman Group (FE) Limited
Printed in Hong Kong
WP/01

**To Valerie**

# Contents

# Preface

Television receivers have in the past few years undergone a rapid transformation in terms of the processing techniques employed and the circuitry used. The use of integrated circuits is only one aspect which has dominated the development of TV receiver design. More fundamental has been the use of digital techniques previously confined to data communication. The use of microprocessors for TV receiver control is another recent development which is widely spread throughout the industry.

For the TV engineer or student, knowledge of highly sophisticated and complex digital processing techniques including microprocessor applications is essential to the understanding of modern TV receiver circuitry. Over a quarter of the book is devoted to these new developments.

I have attempted to describe both the system of television transmission and the circuitry of a TV receiver without undue reliance on previous technical or mathematical knowledge of the reader.

The principles of mono and colour television transmission and reception are described in chapters one and two. This is then followed by detailed analysis of each section of a television receiver (chapters 3 to 14). Circuits using discrete components as well as i.c. chips are fully covered with several practical examples as used by various manufacturers. Digital processing including NICAM, the use of computers and remote control is covered in chapters 15 to 18.

My thanks go to the British TV receiver manufacturers for giving me permission to use their circuits. Particular thanks must go to Ferguson and Philips for their special help and assistance, and I also thank Grundig, Bush and GEC for their valuable help.

K.F. Ibrahim

# 1 Principles of monochrome television

At the television studio, the scene to be transmitted is projected on a photo-sensitive plate located inside the TV camera. The scene is repeatedly scanned by a very fast electron beam which ensures that consecutive images differ only very slightly. At the receiving end, a cathode ray tube (c.r.t.) is used to recreate the picture by an identical process of scanning a screen by an electron beam. The phenomenon of 'persistence of vision' then gives the impression of a moving picture in the same way as a cine film does. In the UK, 25 complete pictures are scanned every second.

## Scanning

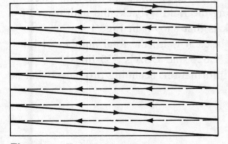

**Fig. 1.1**  Television line scanning

In order to explore the scene in detail the brightness of each element is examined line by line as shown in Fig. 1.1. The electron beam sweeps across the scene from left to right (**the sweep**), returns back very quickly (**the flyback**) to begin scanning the next line and so on. A very large number of lines are employed to give adequate representation of the contents of the picture. In the UK, 625 lines are used while the USA uses 525 lines. The waveform that provides the scanning movement of the electron beam is the sawtooth waveform shown in Fig. 1.2. At the end of each complete scan the electron beam moves back to the top of the scene and the sequence is repeated. In the UK, 25 complete pictures are scanned every second with each picture containing 625 lines. This gives a line frequency of $25 \times 625 = 15\,625$ Hz or 15.625 kHz.

## Interlacing

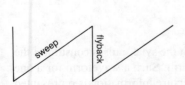

**Fig. 1.2**  Scanning sawtooth waveform

Normal sequential scanning, i.e. scanning complete pictures (625 lines) at one time followed by another complete picture scan, introduces unacceptable flicker. This is avoided by the simple technique known as interlacing. Interlace scanning involves scanning the 'odd' lines 1, 3, 5, etc. first, followed by the 'even' lines 2, 4, 6, etc. Only one half of the picture, known as **a field**, is scanned each time. A complete picture therefore consists of two fields, odd and even, resulting in a field frequency of $2 \times 25 = 50$ Hz.

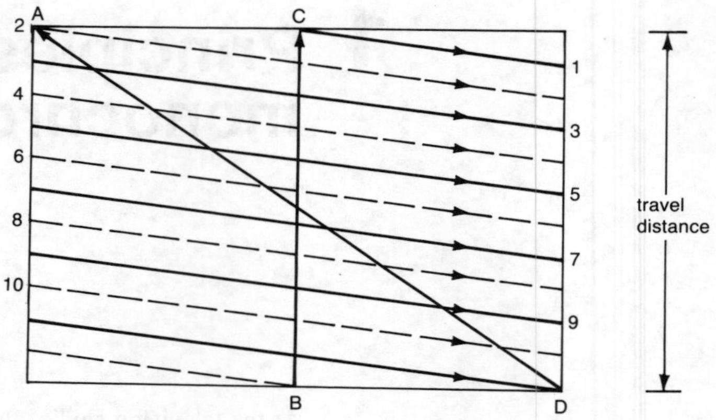

**Fig. 1.3**  Field flyback

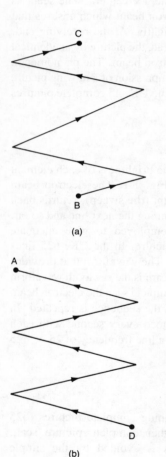

(a)

(b)

**Fig. 1.4**  Field flyback path: (a) end of odd field to start of even field, (b) end of even field to start of odd field

At the end of each field the electron beam is deflected rapidly back to the beginning of the next scan. To ensure equal flyback time for both fields, the flyback is started half way along the last line of the even field, point B in Fig. 1.3, to take the beam to the start of the following odd field at point C half way along line 1. At the end of the odd field the flyback starts at point D, the end of the last line of the odd field, to take the beam to point A, the start of the first line of the even field. As can be seen from Fig. 1.3, the beam is made to move the same vertical distance and hence take the same travel time for both fields. Since the line scan continues to move the electron beam across the screen during the field flyback, the path traced by the beam during the flyback is that shown in Fig. 1.4.

With half a line included in each field, the total number of lines must be odd, hence the UK's 625 and USA's 525 lines.

In the absence of picture information, scanning produces what is known as a **raster**.

### Sync. pulses

For faithful reproduction of the picture by the cathode ray tube, scanning at the receiving end must follow the scanning at the transmitting end, line by line and field by field. To make sure that this takes place, **synchronising pulses** are introduced at the end of each line (**line sync.**) to initiate the line flyback at the receiver. Another synchronising pulse is introduced at the end of a field (**field sync.**) to initiate the start of the field flyback.

### Composite video waveform

The picture information together with the sync. pulses constitutes the composite or complete video waveform. Such a waveform for a one line scan is shown in Fig. 1.5. The picture information is represented by the waveform between the two line sync. pulses and thus may

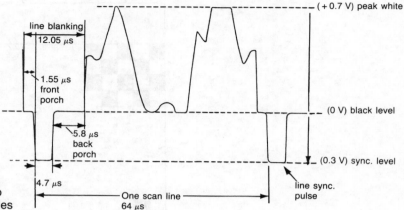

**Fig. 1.5**  One line composite video showing the relative video amplitudes

acquire any shape depending on the varying picture brightness along the line. The waveform shown represents a line that starts at half peak white gradually increasing in brightness to peak white (maximum brightness) back to black then peak white again and finally to half peak white.

The total available voltage is divided into two regions:

below black level region, 0 to $-0.3$ V reserved for the sync. pulses (line and field);
above black level region, 0 to 0.7 V (peak white), used for the video or picture information.

Before and after every sync. pulse the voltage is held at the black level for a short period of time known as the front and back porch respectively. The **front porch** which has a duration of 1.55 $\mu$s ensures that the video information is brought down to the black level before the sync. pulse is applied. The **back porch** which has a longer duration of 5.8 $\mu$s provides time for the flyback to occur before the application of the video information. The back porch is also used for black level clamping. As can be seen the front porch, the sync. pulse and the back porch are at or below the black level. During this time, a total of 12.05 $\mu$s, known as the line blanking period, the video information is completely suppressed.

The duration of one complete line of a composite video waveform may be calculated from the line frequency:

$$\text{line duration} = \frac{1}{\text{line frequency}} = \frac{1}{15.625 \text{ kHz}} = 64 \ \mu\text{s}.$$

### Video bandwidth

The frequency of the video waveform is determined by the change in the brightness of the electron beam as it scans the screen line by line. Maximum video frequency is obtained when adjacent bits or

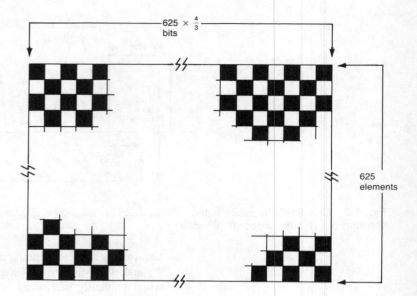

**Fig. 1.6**

elements are alternately black and white as shown in Fig. 1.6, which represents the maximum definition of a TV image. Along a vertical line there are a maximum of 625 alternating black and white elements. For equal definition along a horizontal line there must be the same separation between the black and white bits as there is along a vertical line. For a perfectly square TV screen, an equal number of bits would be obtained in both directions. However, the TV screen has an **aspect ratio** (ratio of width to height) of 4/3. This increases the number of bits along a horizontal line to $625 \times 4/3 = 833.3$ elements per line giving a picture total of

$$625 \times 625 \times 4/3 = 520\,833 \text{ bits or elements.}$$

When an electron beam scans a line containing alternate black and white elements the video waveform is that shown in Fig. 1.7 representing the variation of brightness along the line. As can be seen, for any adjacent pair of black and white elements, one complete cycle is obtained. Hence for the ten elements shown, five complete cycles

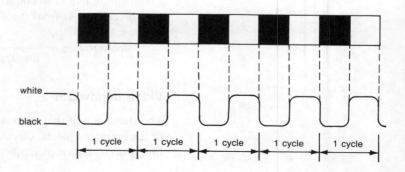

**Fig. 1.7** Video waveform for alternate black and white elements

are produced. It follows that for a complete picture of alternate black and white elements, the number of cycles produced is given by

$$1/2 \times \text{total number of elements} = 1/2 \times 520\,833$$
$$= 260\,417 \text{ cycles per picture}$$

Since there are 25 complete pictures every second, then the number of cycles per second is

$$\text{no. of cycles per picture} \times 25 = 260\,417 \times 25$$
$$= 6\,510\,416\,\text{Hz} = 6.5\,\text{MHz}$$

The minimum video frequency is obtained when the electron beam scans elements of unchanging brightness. This corresponds to an unchanging amplitude of the video waveform, a frequency of 0 Hz or d.c. giving an overall bandwidth of 0 to 6.5 MHz. In practice however, a bandwidth of 0 to 5.5 MHz is found to be satisfactory for domestic applications.

## Modulation

TV transmission uses amplitude modulation for the video information. Ordinary amplitude modulation gives rise to two sets of sidebands on either side of the carrier, thus doubling the bandwidth requirement for the transmission. However, since each sideband contains all the video information, it is possible to suppress one sideband completely, employing what is known as single sideband (SSB) transmission. However, pure single sideband transmission demands a more complicated synchronous detector at the receiving end, making the receiver more expensive. The simple and cheap diode detector introduces a distortion known as **quadrature distortion** caused mainly by the lower end of the video frequency spectrum. To avoid this and still use the diode detector, **vestigial sideband transmission** is employed in which double sideband transmission is used for low video frequencies and single sideband transmission for higher video frequencies. The frequency response of vestigial sideband transmission used in the UK is shown in Fig. 1.8, in which part of the lower sideband, up to 1.25 MHz, together with the unsuppressed upper sideband are transmitted.

As well as the composite video, it is also necessary to transmit a sound signal. Unlike the video information, sound is frequency modulated on a separate carrier with a bandwidth of 100 kHz. The sound carrier is chosen to be 6 MHz away from the vision carrier thus falling just outside the highest transmitted video frequency (Fig. 1.8). Thus for a vision carrier of 510 MHz, the sound carrier is 510 + 6 = 516 MHz.

Referring to Fig. 1.8, it can be seen that the response remains constant over the range of video frequencies up to 5.5 MHz on the upper sideband and 1.25 MHz on the lower sideband. Above 5.5 MHz a sharp but gradual attenuation takes place to ensure that no video

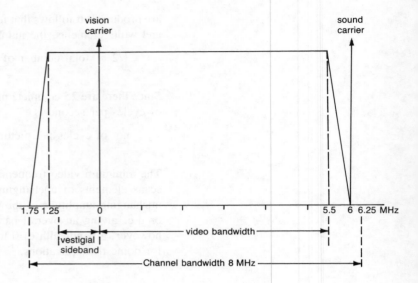

**Fig. 1.8** Frequency response for UK TV transmission

information remains beyond 6 MHz to prevent any overlap with the sound information. An additional 0.25 MHz is needed to accommodate the sound bandwidth and to provide a buffer space for the adjacent channel. Similar attenuation is necessary for frequencies extending beyond 1.25 MHz on the lower sideband to ensure that no video information extends beyond 1.75 MHz, thus preventing any overlap with an adjacent channel. Gradual attenuation is necessary since it is not possible to have filters with instantaneous cut-off characteristics. An 8 MHz (1.75 + 6.25) bandwidth is therefore allocated for each TV channel.

As a consequence of vestigial sideband transmission, video frequencies up to 1.25 MHz are present in both sidebands while frequencies above 1.25 MHz are present in one sideband only. When detected by a simple diode detector, the former will give rise to twice the output of the latter. To compensate for this, it is necessary to shape the frequency response of the receiver so that frequencies that are present in both sidebands are afforded less amplification than those present in one sideband only. Such a response curve is shown in Fig. 1.9.

The video signal may be used to modulate the vision carrier in either a 'positive' or 'negative' way. In the UK, negative modulation is used (Fig. 1.10) with peak white corresponding to a minimum voltage. Positive modulation is shown in Fig. 1.11 which was used in the old 405-line British system. Here peak white corresponds to a maximum voltage.

### Channel allocation

In accordance with the 1961 Stockholm Frequency Plan, each transmitting station is assigned four channels. The Frequency Plan

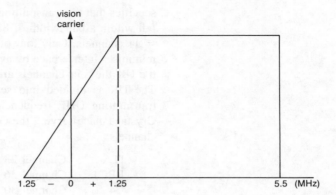

**Fig. 1.9** Television receiver frequency response

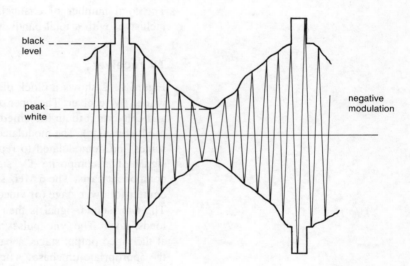

**Fig. 1.10** Negative modulation

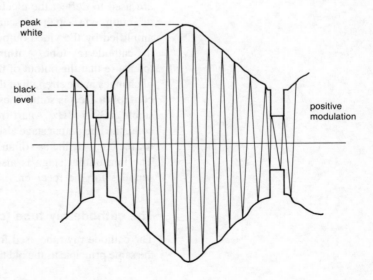

**Fig. 1.11** Positive modulation

specifies that the transmitting frequencies for all four channels must fall within a bandwidth of 88 MHz which embraces a total of 88/8 = 11 channels. Only four of the eight channels may be used which minimises interference by avoiding the use of adjacent channels. In the UK the four channels are BBC 1, BBC 2, ITA and Channel 4. The UK is divided into several areas each served by a station transmitting UHF frequencies in bands IV and V. For example, Crystal Palace serving the Greater London area uses the following channels:

| | | |
|---|---|---|
| ITA | Channel 23 | 486−494 MHz |
| BBC1 | Channel 26 | 510−518 MHz |
| C4 | Channel 30 | 542−550 MHz |
| BBC2 | Channel 33 | 566−574 MHz. |

The total number of channels embraced is 11 (channels 23−33 inclusive) with a total bandwidth of 574−486 = 88 MHz.

## TV receiver

Figure 1.12 shows a block diagram for a monochrome (black and white) TV receiver. The tuner selects an appropriate carrier frequency and converts it to an **intermediate frequency** of 39.5 MHz (mixer-oscillator stage). The modulated i.f. is then amplified through several stages and demodulated to reproduce the original composite video signal. The composite TV signal is then separated into its three component parts. The 6 MHz **sound inter-carrier** is taken off at the emitter follower stage (or video driver stage) following the detector. The f.m. sound signal is then detected, amplified and fed into the loudspeaker. The sync. pulses are clipped from the video information at the video output stage, separated into line and field and taken to the appropriate timebase. After amplification, line and field pulses are used to deflect the electron beam in the horizontal and vertical directions via a pair of scan coils. The video information itself is amplified by the video output amplifier and fed into the cathode of the cathode ray tube. **Automatic gain control (a.g.c.)** is employed to ensure that the output of the i.f. stage remains steady irrespective of changes in the strength of the received signal. **Automatic frequency control (a.f.c.)** is sometimes used to keep the intermediate frquency stable at 39.5 MHz. Apart from providing the drive for the line scan coils, the line output stage also provides the **extra high tension (e.h.t.)** for the c.r.t. by the use of an overwind at the line output transformer. The line output stage is also used to provide other stabilised d.c. supplies for the receiver.

## The cathode ray tube (c.r.t.)

The cathode ray tube used for television picture display operates on the same principle as the old thermionic valve, namely that a negatively

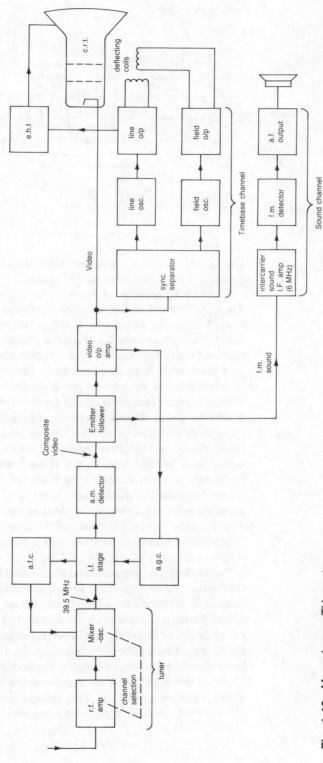

**Fig. 1.12** Monochrome TV receiver

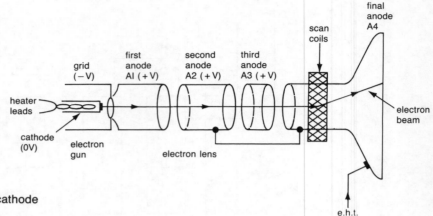

**Fig. 1.13** Monochrome TV cathode ray tube

charged hot cathode emits electrons which are attracted to and collected by a positively charged anode.

In the c.r.t., high-speed electrons are emitted by an electron gun. They are focused and accelerated by an electron lens and directed towards a screen which acts as the positively charged anode (Fig. 1.13). The screen consists of a glass faceplate the inside of which is coated with a fluorescent powder or phosphor which gives a visible glow when hit by high-speed electrons. The colour of the emitted light is determined by the type of phosphor used.

The electron beam generated by the electron gun gives a stationary dot on the screen. In order to produce a display the c.r.t. must have the capacity to deflect the beam in both the horizontal (line) and vertical (field) directions. Electromagnetic deflection is employed using two sets of coils (line and field) known as **scan coils** placed along the neck of the tube in order to deflect the beam horizontally and vertically.

The monochrome display tube consists of a single electron gun, an anode assembly acting as the electron lens and a viewing surface. The function of the electron gun is to produce a high velocity concentrated beam of electrons which strike the phosphor coated screen.

The electrons are attracted and accelerated by a positively charged first anode, A1 in Fig. 1.13, known as the accelerating anode. The number of electrons leaving the cathode are controlled by the grid which, having a negative potential with respect to the cathode, controls the emission of electrons and hence the luminance or brightness of the display. Electron beam suppression, i.e. tube blanking, may thus be obtained by applying a suitable negative-going pulse to the grid. The final anode voltage known as the **extra high tension (e.h.t.)** is in the region of 15–20 kV. This voltage is produced by the use of an overwind on the line output transformer.

# 2 Colour transmission

The first problem facing the transmission of colour TV signals is compatibility with the existing monochrome transmission. Colour TV signals must be capable of producing a normal black and white image on a monochrome receiver without any modification to the television set. Conversely, a colour receiver must be capable of producing a black and white image from a monochrome signal. A colour transmission system must therefore retain the monochrome information, sync. pulses and the sound inter-carrier in the same form as those of normal monochrome transmission. The additional colour information has to be included without interfering with the composite monochrome signal. Furthermore, the colour signal must occupy the same bandwidth as that allocated for monochrome transmission. To understand how this may be done we must isolate the component part of visible light that stimulates the sensation of colour in the human eye.

## Visible light

Visible light is an electromagnetic wave similar to radio waves, X-rays and so on. It forms the narrow band of the electromagnetic wave spectrum shown in Fig. 2.1. Light waves falling on the eye pass through the pupil which focuses the image on the retina at the back of the eye as shown in Fig. 2.2. The retina being sensitive to electromagnetic waves within the visible light band translates the

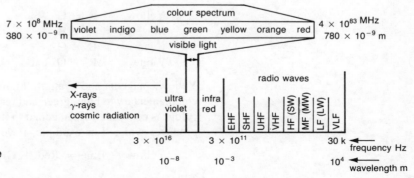

**Fig. 2.1** Electromagnetic wave spectrum

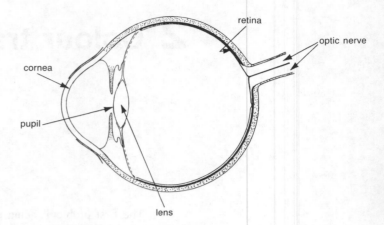

**Fig. 2.2** The human eye

electromagnetic energy into suitable information which is passed to the brain via numerous optic nerve fibres.

The retina contains a large number of light sensitive cells. Some cells known as **rods** are sensitive to brightness (or luminance) only, while others known as **cones** are sensitive to colour (or chrominance) only. The number of rods outnumber the cones by a factor of 20 and are 10 000 times more sensitive. The eye thus reacts predominantly to the luminance of a colour picture and to a much lesser extent to its chrominance. With high video frequencies, for example, fine picture details are perceived in black and white only.

## Primary colours

Cones themselves are of three different types. One type is energised by red, the other by green and the third by blue. These colours are known as **primary colours**. Colours other than the three primary colours are perceived through energising two or more types of cones simultaneously. For example, the sensation of yellow is produced by energising the red and green cones simultaneously. Other colours may be produced by different mixtures of colours. In general all colours may be produced by the addition of appropriate quantities of the three primary colours red R, green G and blue B. This is known as **additive mixing**. For example:

Yellow  = R + G
Magenta = R + B
Cyan    = B + G
White   = R + G + B.

Yellow, magenta and cyan are known as **complementary colours**, complementary to blue, green and red respectively. A complementary colour is one which when added to its corresponding primary colour produces white. For example, if yellow is added to blue, then

Yellow + Blue = Red + Green + Blue = White

Colours may also be produced by a process of **subtractive mixing**. For example, yellow may be produced by subtracting blue from white. Since white, W = R + G + B, then

$$W - B = (R + G + B) - B = R + G = Yellow$$

Similarly,

$$W - G = R + B = magenta$$
$$W - R = G + B = cyan$$
$$W - R - G - B = black \text{ (the absence of colour).}$$

### The colour triangle

A colour triangle (Fig. 2.3) may be used to represent the chrominance content of a colour picture. In the colour triangle, pure white is represented by a point W at the centre of the triangle while other colours are represented by phasors (or vectors) extending from the centre W to a point on or inside the triangle. Phasors going to the three corners of the triangle WR, WG and WB represent pure primary colours, red, green and blue. Other colours are represented by other suitable phasors. For instance, yellow is represented by phasor WY with point Y falling between its two primary components red and green. Similarly for cyan (WC) and magenta (WM).

### Saturation and hue

Phasor WR in Fig. 2.3 represents a completely pure red with no trace of any other colour present. It is said to be **fully saturated**. Desaturation is obtained when white is added to a pure colour. For instance, if white is added to red, desaturated red or pink is produced. On the colour triangle, this is represented by moving along phasor WR away from pure red, R, and towards white, W. Point P1 thus represents desaturated red or pink with WP1 as its phasor representation. A greater desaturation produces a shorter phasor WP2 representing pale pink, and so on. While the length of a phasor represents **saturation**, its direction or angle represents its **hue**. Hue denotes the principal primary component of a colour. For instance, pink has red as its principal primary colour, hence phasor WP is in phase with pure red WR. Yellow, on the other hand, has two primary components, red and green. Hence phasor WY falls between pure red WR and pure green WG. Similarly for other colours such as cyan and magenta. It follows that to represent the chrominance component of a colour picture two qualities have to be ascertained:

> **Hue** which denotes its place on the colour spectrum, e.g red, lemon, moss green and purple, and
> **Saturation** such as pink, pale green, dark blue and other pastel colours.

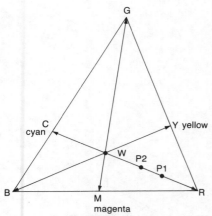

**Fig. 2.3**  Colour triangle

## Principles of colour transmission

Colour transmission involves the simultaneous transmission of the luminance and chrominance components of a colour picture. The luminance signal Y is transmitted directly in the same way as a monochrome system. As for the chrominance component, it is first 'purified' by removing the luminance component from each primary colour, resulting in what is known as **colour difference signals**

$$R - Y$$
$$G - Y \text{ and}$$
$$B - Y$$

Since the luminance signal $Y = R + G + B$, then only two colour difference signals need to be transmitted, namely $R - Y$ and $B - Y$. The third colour difference signal $(G - Y)$ is recovered at the receiving end from the three transmitted components Y, $R - Y$ and $B - Y$:

From $Y = R + G + B$, then
$$R = (R - Y) + Y$$
$$B = (B - Y) + Y \text{ and}$$
$$G = Y - R - B$$

The problem that remains to be solved is the manner in which this additional information, namely $R - Y$ and $B - Y$, may be added to the monochrome signal without causing it any interference. To do this, quadrature amplitude modulation QAM is used on a separate carrier frequency of 4.43 MHz.

## Quadrature amplitude modulation

Two 4.43 MHz carriers, OV and OU, are arranged at right angles (quadrature) to each other as shown in Fig. 2.4. The two colour

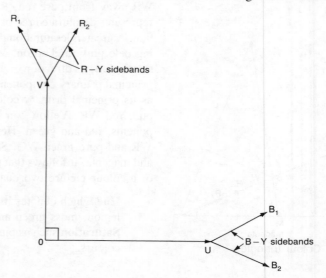

**Fig. 2.4** Quadrature amplitude modulation (QAM)

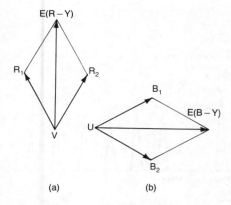

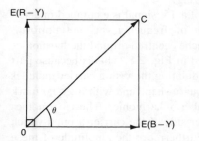

**Fig. 2.5**  Suppressed carrier (QAM)

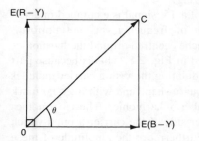

**Fig. 2.6**  Colour difference phasors and their resultant

difference signals are then used to modulate the two carriers with R − Y modulating OV and B − Y modulating OU. As is the case with ordinary amplitude modulation, each modulated carrier produces two bands of side frequencies, one on each side of the carrier. $VR_1/VR_2$ and $UB_1/UB_2$ in Fig. 2.4 represent a pair of side frequencies for the red and blue colour difference signals respectively. The carriers themselves contain no information and thus are suppressed leaving the side frequencies only as shown in phasor form in Fig. 2.5. Each pair of side frequencies $VR_1/VR_2$ and $UB_1/UB_2$ produce resultant colour difference phasors: E(R − Y) and E(B − Y) respectively. The two colour difference phasors retain the 90° or quadrature angle difference. This is because a common frequency of 4.43 MHz is used for both carriers. The two colour difference signals (R − Y) and (B − Y) themselves produce a resultant chrominance phasor OC (Fig. 2.6). Although the carrier itself is suppressed, the resultant phasor has the same frequency as the suppressed carrier. This chrominance phasor corresponds to the phasor associated with the colour triangle with its length (or amplitude) representing saturation and its angle (or phase) θ representing hue.

The bandwidth of the chrominance information is limited to approximately 1 MHz on each side of the colour carrier which is now referred to as a **subcarrier** since it falls within the TV transmission frequency spectrum as shown in Fig. 2.7. The relatively narrow bandwidth allocated to the chrominance is quite sufficient for an adequate reproduction of a colour image at the receiving end. This is because, as stated earlier, the eye perceives high video frequencies in black and white only.

## Frequency interleaving

The colour subcarrier is chosen to fall within the monochrome frequency spectrum to avoid an increase in the bandwidth of TV transmission. There is thus an overlap between the chrominance and part of the luminance signals which would create patterning on a

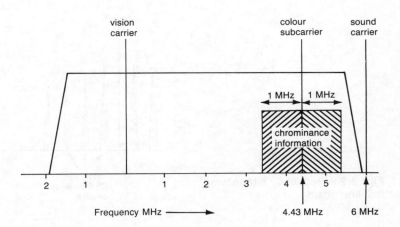

**Fig. 2.7**  Frequency spectrum for colour TV transmission

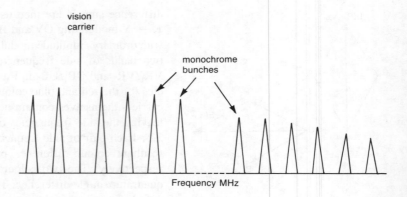

**Fig. 2.8**  Side frequency bunching

monochrome receiver tuned to a colour transmission. This is avoided by the use of frequency interleaving.

When the frequency spectrum of a TV signal is examined in detail it is found that the distribution of frequencies is not uniform. Frequencies tend to gather in bunches centred around the harmonics of the line frequency as illustrated in Fig. 2.8. This is because part of the composite video signal modulating the vision carrier includes the line sync. pulses which, of square shape and with unequal mark and space, contain an infinite number of harmonics. These harmonics produce side frequencies on either side of the carrier around which the video information clusters. Furthermore the amplitude of these side frequencies gets progressively smaller as we move away from the vision carrier. It follows that for minimum interference with the monochrome signal, the subcarrier must fall between two bunches. The subcarrier is itself amplitude modulated by the chrominance signal and thus produces side frequencies of its own in similar bunches on each side of the subcarrier centred around harmonics of the line frequency. By choosing a subcarrier to fall between two monochrome bunches, the chrominance bunches will then fall in the spaces between the bunches produced by the monochrome signal (Fig. 2.9). This is known as **frequency interleaving** or **interlacing**.

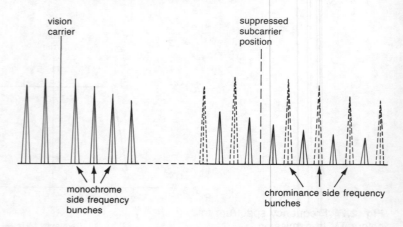

**Fig. 2.9**  Frequency interleaving, half-line offset

The subcarrier must therefore be a multiple of half line frequency, known as half-line offset. However, to avoid any possible dot pattern on a monochrome receiver quarter-line offset is used with the subcarrier a multiple of a quarter-line frequency. This is further modified by the addition of half-field frequency giving a subcarrier frequency of 4.433 618 75 MHz.

## Composite colour signal

The modulated subcarrier is added to the luminance (monochrome) signal to form the composite colour signal shown in Fig. 2.10. The modulated subcarrier appears as a sine wave superimposed on the monochrome signal which is changing in amplitude and phase. The amplitude of the subcarrier represents saturation. Thus a fully saturated colour is represented by maximum subcarrier amplitude and black and white by zero subcarrier amplitude. Hue on the other hand is represented by the phase angle of the subcarrier. To ascertain the phase angle, a 'burst' of about 10 cycles of the original subcarrier is transmitted for use as a reference at the receiver. This **colour burst** is mounted on the back porch of the line sync. as shown. The phase of the modulated colour signal is then compared with that of the regenerated subcarrier to provide a measure of the phase angle and therefore hue. The absence of a colour burst indicates a black and white transmission.

## Gamma correction

Receiver cathode ray tubes use the voltage at the grid to control the beam current and hence the brightness of the display on the screen.

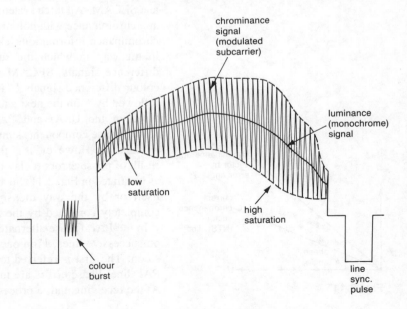

**Fig. 2.10** One line of composite colour signal

However, the relationship between the two suffers from a non-linearity that must be corrected to avoid severe deterioration in the quality of the picture. This non-linearity at the receiving end is compensated for by the introduction of an equal and opposite non-linearity at the transmitting end known as gamma-correction ($\gamma$-correction). The voltage from the camera is raised to a power of $1/\gamma$ ($E^{1/\gamma}$), where for UK TV transmission $\gamma = 2.2$ and $1/\gamma = 0.45$. Gamma-corrected signals are identified by a dash, e.g. Y′, R′ and gamma-corrected colour difference signals are indicated as Y′ − R′ and Y′ − B′.

### Weighting factors

As already stated, the subcarrier has a maximum amplitude when 100% or fully saturated colour is transmitted. Since the subcarrier is added to the luminance signal, the amplitude of the composite colour signal may exceed the maximum possible voltage. To avoid this, the peak amplitude of the chrominance signal, i.e. the peak amplitude of the colour difference signals, is reduced by a factor known as the weighting factor. The new weighted components of chrominance signal are referred to as $U$ and $V$ where

$$U = 0.493 \ (B′ - Y′) \text{ and}$$
$$V = 0.877 \ (R′ - Y′).$$

The resultant chrominance phasor is now produced by the phasor sum of $U$ and $V$.

### PAL colour system

There are three main systems of colour transmission: the NTSC, PAL and SECAM. All three systems split the colour picture into luminance and chrominance with colour difference signals used to transmit the chrominance information. The difference between the systems lies in the way in which the subcarrier is modulated by the colour difference signals. SECAM which is used in France transmits the colour difference signals $U$ and $V$ on alternate lines, $U$ on one line followed by $V$ on the next and so on. The other two systems, NTSC (used in the USA) and PAL (used in the UK), transmit both chrominance components simultaneously using quadrature amplitude modulation. However, it is found that errors in hue may occur as a result of phase errors (delay or advance) of the chrominance phasor as illustrated in Fig. 2.11. Such errors are caused either by the receiver itself or by the way the signal is propagated. They are almost completely corrected by the PAL system.

In the PAL (phase alternate line) system, the $V$ signal is reversed on successive lines, $V$ on one line followed by $-V$ on the next and so on. The first is referred to as an NTSC line and the second as a PAL line. Phase errors are thus reversed from one line to the next. At the receiving end, a process of averaging of consecutive lines by

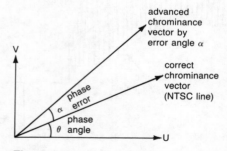

**Fig. 2.11**

the eye cancels out the errors to reproduce the correct hue. This simple method is known as PAL-S. A more accurate method is the use of a delay line to allow for consecutive lines (NTSC and PAL) to be added to each other thus cancelling phase errors. This is known as PAL-D.

In order to distinguish between the two types of lines the colour burst is made to swing by approximately 180° as a NTSC line is followed by a PAL line and back again.

### Colour TV receiver

Figure 2.12 shows a generalised block diagram of the colour processing parts of a PAL TV receiver.

After detection, the composite colour signal is fed into three processing sections: burst, luminance and chrominance.

### Burst processing

The burst section provides the necessary reference subcarrier frequency, colour kill and burst blanking signals. The burst gate amplifier is opened by a line sync. pulse from the line timebase (Fig. 2.12) allowing only the colour burst to go through. The burst is fed into a phase discriminator and a reactance stage in order to phase lock

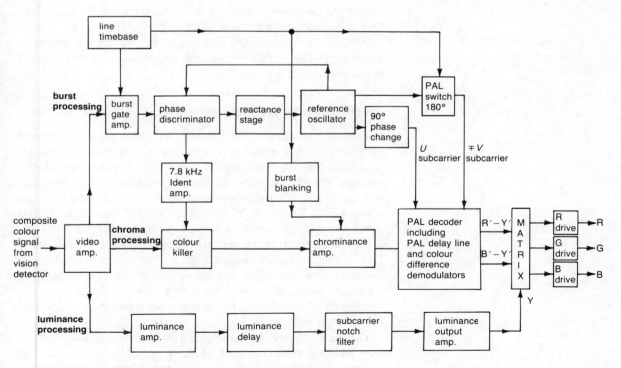

**Fig. 2.12**   Colour TV receiver

the crystal-controlled reference oscillator to that of the original suppressed subcarrier. Two quadrature (90°) 4.43 MHz subcarriers are necessary for the two colour difference demodulators. For this reason one output of the oscillator is made to suffer a 90° phase change before going into the B′ − Y′ ($U$ component) demodulator. The other output is fed directly to the R′ − Y′ ($V$ component) demodulator. However, since the phase of the $V$ component is reversed on alternate lines, a PAL switch is introduced as shown to ensure that the phase of the $V$ subcarrier changes by 180° in step with the transmitted signal.

The burst which is present on colour transmission only changes phase from one line to the next. This change in phase produces a half-line frequency at the phase discriminator stage, i.e. a frequency of 7.8 kHz known as the **ident signal**. The absence of the ident signal indicates a monochrome-only transmission. The **colour kill** is then activated to shut the chrominance processing channel. This is essential in order to prevent information from the luminance signal which falls within the chrominance bandwidth from getting through the chrominance channel causing colour interference on the screen.

## Luminance processing

After amplification, the signal is delayed to compensate for the delay introduced to the chrominance component by the relatively narrow-band chrominance amplifier. The **delay line** ensures that both the luminance and chrominance signals reach the c.r.t. at the same time. The modulated colour subcarrier which contains the colour information is then removed by a notch filter leaving the luminance signal only. This is then fed into the output amplifier before going to the matrix and the c.r.t.

## Chrominance (or chroma) processing

For colour transmission, the colour killer allows the signal through to the chrominance amplifier. The chrominance amplifier is preceded by a band pass filter which allows only colour information to pass through. The PAL decoder includes two synchronous demodulators, one for the B′ − Y′ and the other for the R′ − Y′ components of the colour signal. The B′ − Y′ demodulator is fed with the 4.43 MHz subcarrier directly from the reference oscillator while the R′ − Y′ demodulator receives the subcarrier signal via a PAL switch. In PAL-D receivers a chrominance delay line is incorporated in the decoder unit which stores one line of chrominance information for a one line period of 64 $\mu$s. This is then added to the chrominance component of the following line to cancel out errors in hue introduced by incorrect pulse angles.

The chrominance amplifier is turned off for the duration of the burst by a blanking pulse (**burst blanking**) from the line timebase. This prevents the burst from creating colour interference on the screen.

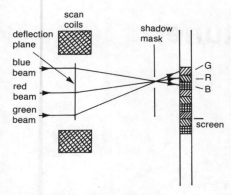

**Fig. 2.13**   Colour tube colour production

## Colour tube

The cathode ray tubes used for colour display have three separate guns arranged to bombard a screen which is coated with three different types of phosphors, one for each primary colour. The three phosphors are arranged to form a 3-colour triad. A steel **shadow mask** is placed behind the coated screen which allows the three electron beams to converge and pass through slots before they strike their respective phosphor on the screen as shown in Fig. 2.13. The shadow mask is designed so that each electron beam strikes only its own particular phosphor (blue gun for blue phosphor and so on) and no other as the deflection (scan) coils cause the beams to scan the screen. Three primary colours are thus produced which, because they are very close to each other, are not resolved individually by the human eye. Instead an additive mixture is perceived giving the sensation of colour.

## Tube drive

There are two colour tube drive techniques: RGB and colour difference. In the RGB technique, the output Y of the luminance section and the two colour difference outputs, $B' - Y'$ and $R' - Y'$ from the chrominance section are fed into a matrix to reproduce the three primary colours R, G and B which after amplifcation are used to drive the cathodes of the colour tube. Alternatively the colour tube may be driven directly by the colour difference signals, $R - Y$, $G - Y$ and $B - Y$, with luminance Y going into the grid to perform the subtraction process. The former technique is almost universally used by manufacturers.

# 3 The UHF tuner

The function of the tuner is to select a TV channel frequency, amplify it and convert it into an intermediate frequency for further amplification by the i.f. stage (Fig. 3.1). The tuner must be capable of selecting any channel from bands IV and V, provide sufficient r.f. amplification with good signal-to-noise ratio and minimal frequency drift. One or more stages of r.f. amplification are therefore necessary before the mixer oscillator stage. A high-pass filter is normally used at the input to the r.f. amplifier to produce a correctly shaped response curve. The mixer-oscillator changes the tuned r.f. to a common **intermediate frequency**, i.f. of 39.5 MHz. The tuner unit is built inside a metal case to screen it from outside r.f. interference. Further screening is also provided between various stages of the unit by metal walls. These inner walls which form part of the tuned circuits prevent unwanted coupling between one compartment and another. Where coupling is needed, a small hole or slot is cut in the dividing wall which then act as a coupling capacitor.

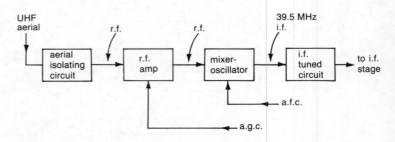

**Fig. 3.1**  UHF tuner

## UHF tuned circuits

The resonant frequency of a tuned circuit is given as

$$f = \frac{1}{2\pi\sqrt{LC}}$$

Due to the high carrier frequencies employed in TV transmission (370–862 MHz) the values of $L$ and $C$ are very small, with the result that normal inductors and capacitors cannot be used. Instead, conductors known as tuned or **lecher lines** are employed. These are short transmission lines, normally a quarter of a wavelength long which, in combination with a tuning capacitor, resonate at the required frequency. Coupling between stages is achieved by simple loops of wire or by tapping the tuned line.

### Aerial isolation

The aerial is usually connected to the tuner via an isolating circuit. This is essential in receivers operating from the mains without the use of an isolating transformer. If the receiver was to be fed directly from the mains, then the chassis may be live and if it was connected directly to the aerial would make the aerial live as well.

A commonly used aerial isolation circuit is shown in Fig. 3.2.

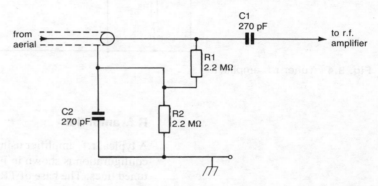

**Fig. 3.2** Aerial isolation circuit

Capacitors C1 and C2 are large enough to give adequate coupling for radio frequencies, but of high enough impedance at the mains frequency of 50 Hz to effectively isolate the aerial from the mains supply. Resistors R1 and R2 prevent static charge from building up on the aerial.

### R.f. oscillator

At the frequencies of operation within the u.h.f. range, feedback in the oscillator is obtained by mutual inductance employing tuned lines to form a Hartley or a Collpit oscillator. Use may also be made of the inter-electrode capacitors of the transistor as shown in Fig. 3.3. The circuit shows a common base Collpit oscillator in which inter-electrode capacitors $C_{ce}$ (between collector and emitter) and $C_{be}$ (between emitter and base) provide the necessary feedback for sustained oscillation. $C_{ce}$ in series with $C_{be}$ effectively fall across the output developed between the collector and base. Part of this output, that across $C_{be}$, is fed back into the input between the emitter and base. R1 is the emitter resistor, R2/R3 is the base bias chain with C2 as the base or bias decoupling capacitor, TL1 is the output tuned line resonating with variable capacitor C3.

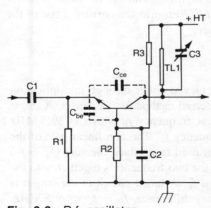

**Fig. 3.3** R.f. oscillator

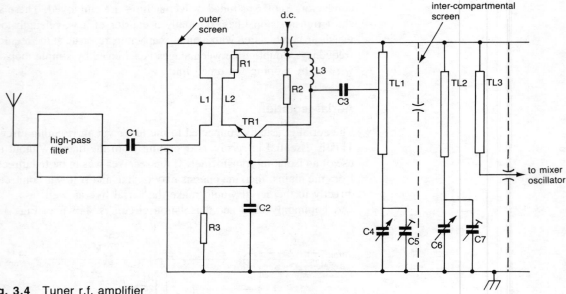

**Fig. 3.4** Tuner r.f. amplifier

### R.f. amplifier

A typical r.f. amplifier using npn transistor TR1 in the common base configuration is shown in Fig. 3.4, in which TL1, TL2 and TL3 are tuned lines. The base of TR1 is decoupled to the chassis by capacitor C2 with potential divider R2/R3 providing the base bias. R1 is the emitter resistor for d.c. stability and L3 is an r.f. choke. Loops L1/L2 provide the input coupling with the output developing across resonant circuit TL1/C4 and trimmer C5. The signal is then coupled to the second tuned line TL2 through the small gaps in the screening between the two stages. TL2 which is tuned by C6 and trimmed by C7 acts as a bandpass coupling element between TL1 and TL3 which feeds the mixer-oscillator stage. The high-pass filter at the input together with bandpass element TL2/C6/C7 ensures the correct shape of the frequency response of the tuner.

### Mixer-oscillator

Frequency changing may be achieved either through multiplication or addition. The latter is the preferred method for TV tuners. A single transistor is made to oscillate at frequency $f_0$ which is 39.5 MHz above the selected channel frequency $f_c$. The non-linear part of the transistor characteristics is then used to produce the sum $(f_0 + f_c)$ and the difference $(f_0 - f_c)$ of the two frequencies together with the two original frequencies, $f_0$ and $f_c$. A tuned circuit at the output is then made to select the frequency difference, $f_0 - f_c = 39.5$ MHz.

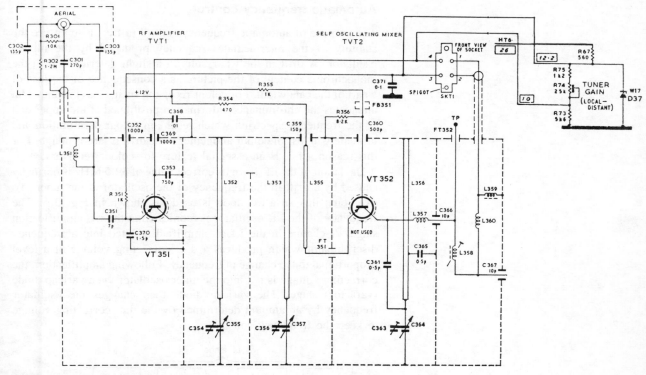

**Fig. 3.5**  Mechanical UHF tuner
(Ferguson)

## Complete UHF tuner

A typical tuner used for a monochrome TV receiver employing
mechanical push button tuning is shown in Fig. 3.5. VT351 and
VT352 are the r.f amplifier and the mixer-oscillator respectively. Both
are connected in the common base configuration. The signal from
the aerial is fed through an isolating circuit via coupling capacitor
C351 into the emitter of VT351 with R351 as the emitter resistor.
The output of the r.f. amplifier across tuned circuit L352/C354/C355
is transformer-coupled (via bandpass coupling circuit L353/C356/
C357) to coupling loop L355 at the input of the mixer-oscillator
transistor VT352. The output is taken at the collector of VT352
via filter components L357/C366. The i.f. is produced across L358
which is tuned to 39.5 MHz. L359/L360 together with the input
circuit of the first i.f. amplifier form a bandpass filter allowing the
video bandwidth to go through.

The gain of the r.f. amplifier may be varied by local distance gain
control R74 which controls the base voltage of VT351 and hence its
gain. Resistor R74 is normally set for maximum gain. However in
strong reception areas the r.f. amplifier may saturate causing clipping
and hence distortion of the signal. In such cases the gain of the
amplifier is reduced.

## Automatic frequency control

The purpose of automatic frequency control (a.f.c.) is to ensure the stability of the intermediate frequency produced by the mixer-oscillator. A drift in the i.f. results in a slight deterioration in the monochrome content of the picture as a consequence of the loss of a part of the bandwidth. For colour reception such a loss in bandwidth attenuates the chrominance information positioned at the upper end of the frequency spectrum which results in colour desaturation and ultimately in loss of colour altogether if the drift is large enough. For this reason a.f.c. is an essential feature for colour receivers.

Deviation of the i.f. from its correct value of 39.5 MHz is normally caused by a drift in the frequency of the oscillator at the tuner. To overcome this an a.f.c. loop is used, as shown in Fig. 3.6. The frequency of the i.f. oscillator is monitored at the i.f. amplification stage. A change in the i.f. is amplified and fed into a frequency discriminator which produces a d.c. correcting voltage of a level proportional to the change in frequency. Following amplification, the correcting voltage is fed into the tuner oscillator via a varicap diode (varactor) stage. The varicap diode then changes the óscillator frequency by an amount determined by the d.c. correcting voltage to keep the frequency constant.

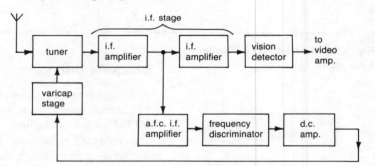

**Fig. 3.6** Automatic frequency control (a.f.c.) loop

An a.f.c. switch is normally incorporated in order to disable (i.e. disconnect) the a.f.c. loop when the receiver is being tuned. The disabling switch, sometimes known as an **a.f.c. mute**, allows tuning to take place independently of the loop, thus ensuring that the frequency discriminator is operating at the centre point of its characteristics in order that it may be able to correct frequency deviations on either side of the i.f. An a.f.c. mute is sometimes used for changing channels to prevent what is known as **'lock out'** of the signal. This is caused by the inability of the a.f.c. to change as quickly as the channel selection system. A.f.c. disabling switches are either operated manually or automatically when a channel is selected.

## Varicap tuners

Varicap tuners are widely used in modern TV receivers. Compared with the ganged-capacitor type, varicap tuners are more reliable, have no moving parts and hence are less prone to frequency drift, are more suitable for touch-sensitive tuning and remote control and may be located in the most suitable place on the chassis with only the control panel having to be on the front cabinet of the receiver.

A typical switching arrangement for a varicap tuner is shown in Fig. 3.7. Varicap diode W1 acts as the tuning capacitor for lecher line L1. The reverse voltage for W1 is provided by preset tuning control resistors R1, R2 or R3 depending on the channel selected. A variation of approximately 30 V would tune the receiver through all channels in bands IV and V. To ensure frequency stability, a stabilised d.c. supply is used as well as thermistors in some cases to compensate for changes in d.c. voltages due to temperature variation. Where more than one varicap diode is used, such diodes must be matched, i.e. must have identical characteristics.

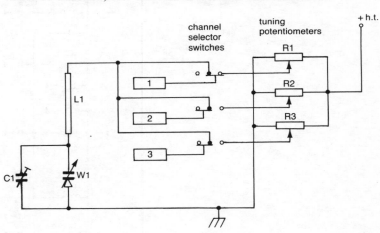

**Fig. 3.7** Varicap switching arrangement channel 1 selected

An example of a varicap tuner used in a colour TV receiver is shown in Fig. 3.8. The tuning voltage from the channel selector is fed to the cathode of four matched tuning varactors at pins 2, 6 and 11 ($U_{\text{Abst Tun}}$) via their respective 22K resistors; R02, R16 and R36. The aerial is connected to pin 1 (ANT) with the i.f. output appearing at pin 10 ($ZF_{\text{out}}$). The i.f. is also available at pin 13 which is used to feed an a.f.c. system. Field effect transistor T07 is the r.f. amplifier and common-base T28 is the mixer-oscillator. L14/L18 and associated circuitry provide bandpass coupling.

## The phase-locked loop, PLL

Modern TV tuners invariably use phase-locked loop to ensure stability of the i.f. output avoiding the use of an a.f.c. loop. Available in integrated circuit packages, the phase-locked loop is today widely used

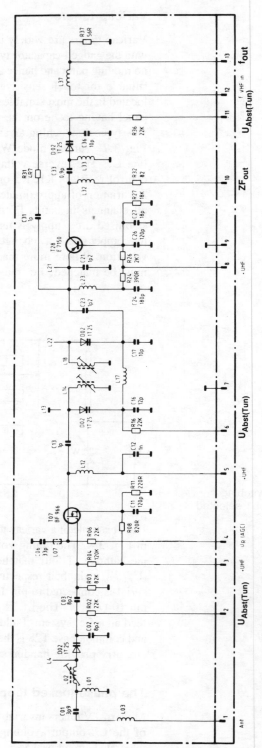

**Fig. 3.8** Varicap UHF tuner (Ferguson)

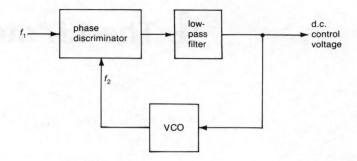

**Fig. 3.9**  Phase-locked loop, PLL

in a variety of electronic applications including chrominance decoding. As illustrated in Fig. 3.9, the phase-locked loop consists of a phase discriminator or detector, low pass loop filter and a voltage-controlled oscillator, VCO. Without an input signal to the phase discriminator, the VCO is free-running at its own natural frequency, $f_2$. When a signal arrives, the phase discriminator compares the input frequency $f_1$ with that of the VCO. A difference results in a d.c. output which after filtering is fed back into the VCO to change its frequency. The process continues until the two frequencies are equal and the PLL is said to be locked.

### Synthesised tuning

In the synthesised tuner, the tuning voltage is supplied from a phase-locked loop as shown in Fig. 3.10. A sample of the tuner output frequency is fed back to the phase discriminator via a controlled divider, $\div n$, known as a pre-scaler. The value of pre-scaler factor $n$ is set by the channel select input. The value of $n$ determines frequency $f_1$ going into the phase discriminator. The discriminator then compares $f_1$ with reference frequency $f_r$. A d.c. output is produced reflecting the difference between the two frequencies. After filtering, this d.c. voltage is then used to tune the tuner to the selected channel.

Synthesised PLL-controlled tuners have extremely stable output with practically no drift, thus removing the need for an a.f.c. circuit. The stability of the tuner output depends to a large extent on the the stability of the reference frequency. For this reason frequency divider $\div N$ is used to divide the frequency of a crystal controlled reference oscillator by a large factor which improves stability by the same factor $N$.

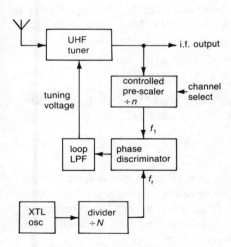

**Fig. 3.10**  Synthesised tuner

# 4 The i.f. stage

It will be recalled that the intermediate frequency is derived at the mixer-oscillator stage of the tuner. The local oscillator is made to oscillate at a frequency which is 39.5 MHz greater than the selected carrier frequency. The intermediate frequency is then obtained by selecting the difference between the carrier and the oscillator frequencies. For example, if the TV receiver is tuned to a channel frequency of 511.25 MHz (BBC1 transmission from Crystal Palace) then the oscillator must be tuned to frequency $f_0 = 511.25 + 39.5 = 550.75$ MHz. Similarly for other carrier frequencies. The relative position of the various frequencies of a modulated u.h.f. carrier is displayed in a frequency spectrum.

The frequency spectrum for a modulated 511.25 MHz carrier is shown in Fig. 4.1(a). The 8 MHz bandwidth extends from $f_{min}$ to $f_{max}$ where

$$f_{min} = 511.25 - 1.75 = 509.5 \text{ MHz and}$$
$$f_{max} = 511.25 + 6.25 = 517.5 \text{ MHz.}$$

And the sound carrier being 6 MHz above the vision carrier has a frequency of $511.25 + 6.00 = 517.25$ MHz.

## The i.f. spectrum

After the mixer-oscillator stage, the vision carrier is replaced by an i.f. of 39.5 MHz giving the intermediate frequency spectrum shown in Fig. 4.1(b) in which every frequency is the difference between $f_0$, the local oscillator frequency and the original in (a). Thus the sound carrier is translated into a sound i.f. of

$$f_0 - \text{sound carrier} = 550.75 - 517.25 = 33.5 \text{ MHz}$$

The sound i.f. is now 6 MHz below the vision i.f. Similarly all other frequencies will reverse their position when they are converted to their equivalent on the i.f. spectrum as shown in Fig. 4.1(b).

## The i.f. response curve

Apart from providing sufficient i.f. amplification to drive the detector,

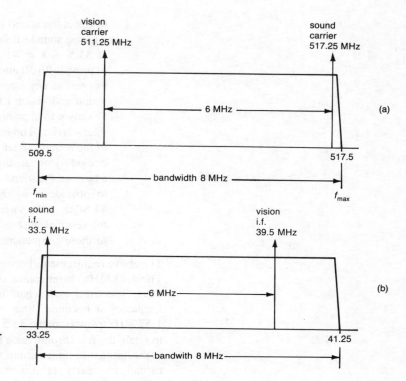

vision
carrier
511.25 MHz

sound
carrier
517.25 MHz

6 MHz

(a)

509.5

517.5

bandwidth 8 MHz

$f_{min}$

$f_{max}$

sound
i.f.
33.5 MHz

vision
i.f.
39.5 MHz

6 MHz

(b)

33.25

41.25

bandwith 8 MHz

**Fig. 4.1** (a) Frequency spectrum for a modulated 511.25 MHz carrier, (b) Intermediate frequency spectrum

the i.f. stage is required to shape the frequency response of the received signal to that shown in Fig. 4.2. The purpose of the i.f. response curve is

1. to reject the vision i.f. of the adjacent higher channel. The adjacent vision i.f. falls 8 MHz below the vision i.f. at $39.5 - 8 = 31.5$ MHz.

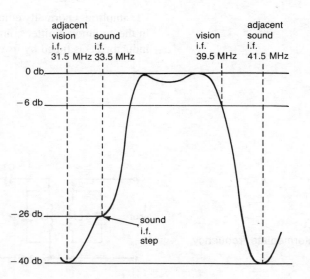

adjacent
vision
i.f.
31.5 MHz

sound
i.f.
33.5 MHz

vision
i.f.
39.5 MHz

adjacent
sound
i.f.
41.5 MHz

0 db

−6 db

−26 db

sound
i.f.
step

−40 db

**Fig. 4.2** Intermediate frequency reponse curve

2. to reject the sound i.f. of the adjacent lower channel. The adjacent sound i.f. falls 8 MHz above the sound inter-carrier at $33.5 + 8 = 41.5$ MHz.
3. to provide 26 dB attenuation at 33.5 MHz. This is necessary to prevent any interference caused by a beat between the sound and vision i.f.s. A small step or ledge is provided as shown to accommodate the f.m. deviation of the sound inter-carrier. The f.m. step prevents amplitude modulation of the sound carrier which would be detected by the vision demodulator causing a pattern to appear on the screen and a buzz on the sound, a symptom known as **sound on vision**.
4. to provide a steady fall in amplitude from 38 MHz to 41 MHz at the vision i.f. end. This is necessary because the vestigial sideband transmission gives increased emphasis to these frequencies.

The above requirements become very critical in colour TV reception. The 4.43 MHz chrominance subcarrier falls at the higher end of the video spectrum and when this is converted to an intermediate frequency it becomes $39.5 - 4.43 = 35.07$ MHz which is only 1.57 MHz away from the 33.5 MHz sound i.f. It follows that in order to retain the full chrominance information and its correct relationship to the luminance information, the response curve must not be allowed to fall too early at this end thus restricting the chrominance information, while at the same time it must provide sufficient rejection of the sound i.f. Failure to do this produces cross modulation between the 4.43 MHz chrominance subcarrier and the 6 MHz sound inter-carrier. This cross modulation appears as a 1.57 MHz $(6.00 - 4.43)$ pattern on the screen known as **herring-bone** pattern.

### The i.f. amplifier

I.f. amplifiers normally employ high-frequency transistors connected in the common emitter configuration as shown in Fig. 4.3 in which inductor L3 is tuned by its own self capacitance. A common emitter

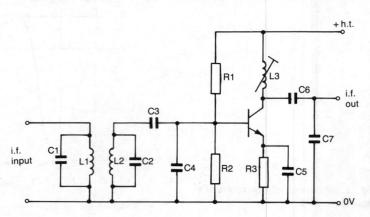

**Fig. 4.3** Intermediate frequency amplifier

amplifier has a low input impedance which shunts the input signal from the preceding stage, an effect known as the **damping** effect. To minimise this, tapped-capacitor or tapped-inductor coupling is used. In Fig. 4.3, capacitor chain C3/C4 is a **tapped-capacitor** coupling network which reduces the damping effect on tuned circuit L2/C2. If Rp is the input resistance of the transistor, then the effective shunting or damping resistance Rs appearing across the tuned circuit is

$$Rs = \left( \frac{C3+C4}{C3} \right)^2 Rp$$

Chain C6/C7 is another tapped-capacitor coupling at the output.

For a tapped-inductor coupling (Fig. 4.4), the relationship between Rs and Rp is

$$Rs = \left( \frac{L1+L2}{L2} \right)^2 Rp$$

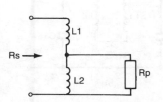

**Fig. 4.4** Tapped inductor coupling

### Staggered tuning

Vision i.f. amplifiers are required to have high gain over a wide bandwidth. This cannot be satisfied by the use of simple tuned circuits which have the response curve shown in Fig. 4.5. Since the product of gain and bandwidth is constant it follows that any attempt to increase the bandwidth will result in a reduced gain and vice versa. A high Q tuned circuit provides higher gain coupled with narrower bandwidth, while a low Q circuit gives increased bandwidth with lower gain. To obtain adequate bandwidth with sufficient amplification **staggered** tuning may be used.

Instead of using identical tuned circuits for each i.f. amplifier, the tuning frequencies are staggered by tuning each stage to a different frequency. The effect of this on a 3-stage i.f. strip is shown in Fig. 4.6. The response curves overlap giving an overall resultant curve combining both high gain and wide bandwidth. By spacing the tuning frequencies and using different Q-factors various shapes may be produced.

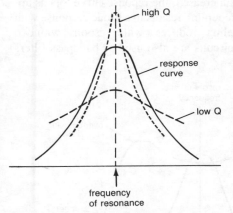

**Fig. 4.5** Frequency response of a tuned circuit

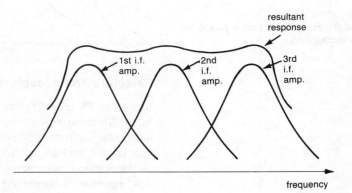

**Fig. 4.6** Staggered tuning

## Overcoupling

An alternative to staggered tuning is the use of inductance or capacitive overcoupling. Figure 4.7 shows two types of capacitor overcoupling.

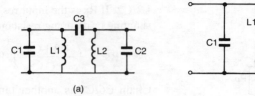

**Fig. 4.7** Overcoupling: (a) top capacitor coupling, (b) shunt capacitor coupling

Top capacitor coupling is shown in (a) in which C3 is used to increase the coupling between the primary and secondary of the transformer. This methiod is also known as series capacitor coupling. In (b) capacitor C2 provides the increased coupling between the two windings of the transformer. This method is known as shunt capacitor coupling. As the coupling is increased, the reponse curve 'opens up' as shown in Fig. 4.8. Undercoupling results in a broad response with a single peak while overcoupling produces a wider response with two peaks. Overcoupled tuned circuits are also used as bandpass filters or transformers.

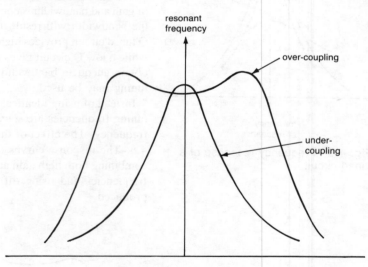

**Fig. 4.8** Response curve produced by overcoupling

## Rejectors and acceptors

In modern TV receivers fixed tuned wideband i.f. amplifiers are used in the form of discrete components or are incorporated within individual integrated circuits. The shaping of the response curve is then carried out by a selectivity network consisting of what is known as rejector/acceptor circuits forming a complicated filter unit.

A **rejector** is a parallel-tuned circuit whose impedance is a

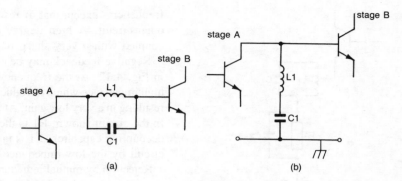

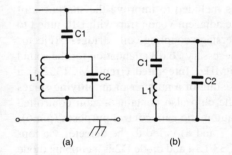

**Fig. 4.9**  Rejector circuits

**Fig. 4.10**  Series/shunt frequency
trap circuits

maximum at the frequency of resonance. An **acceptor** on the other hand is a series tuned circuit with a minimum impedance at the resonant frequency.

In Fig. 4.9(a) the parallel-tuned circuit L1/C1 inserted between two amplifier stages presents a high impedance at resonance frequency thus 'rejecting' that frequency. For frequencies other than the resonant frequency the tuned circuit represents a low impedance allowing these signals to flow unaffected. The same effect may be produced by the series tuned circuit connected as shown in Fig. 4.9(b). At resonance, the tuned circuit presents a very low impedance thus shorting out these frequencies to chassis. Other frequencies remain unaffected. These circuits are generally known as **traps**.

To improve the sharpness of a trap circuit, series shunt-tuned or shunt series-tuned circuits are used as shown in Fig. 4.10. These circuits provide frequency emphasis as well as rejection to accommodate the necessary sharpness of the response curve. In Fig. 4.10(a) L1C2 are chosen to have an inductive reactance at the rejected frequency. This inductive reactance resonates with C1 to form an acceptor, trapping signals at that frequency. The frequency of resonance of parallel tuned circuit L1C2 itself is emphasised since it offers very high impedance to signals at that frequency. A similar effect is obtained from the circuit in Fig. 4.10(b) with L1C1 forming an acceptor and L1C1C2 forming a rejector.

Other rejector circuits using Bridge-T combinations are shown in Fig. 4.11. In each case the circuit appears as a short circuit for all

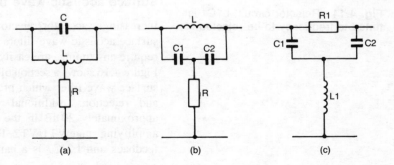

**Fig. 4.11**  Bridge-T rejector circuits

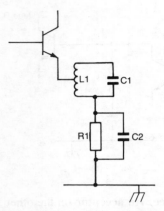

**Fig. 4.12** Negative feedback rejection

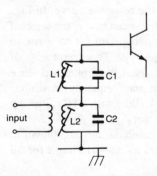

**Fig. 4.13** Mutual inductance rejector circuit

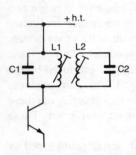

**Fig. 4.14** Rejector circuit. L1C1 is tuned to frequency to be rejected

frequencies except that of resonance in which case it appears as an open circuit. A high degree of attenuation may thus be obtained coupled with a very sharp response.

Negative feedback may be employed in rejector circuits as shown in Fig. 4.12. At the frequency of resonance, L1C1 presents a very high impedance which introduces a large amount of negative feedback resulting in a very low gain. At all other frequencies the gain is normal. In the circuit shown, R1 is the normal emitter resistor and C2 is its decoupling capacitor. L1 is tapped to prevent damping of the tuned circuit by the low impedance of the transistor.

Rejection by mutual inductance is shown in Fig. 4.13. L2C2 offers a very low impedance path to signals at its resonant frequency which, due to the mutual inductance between L1 and L2, absorbs a large amount of energy away from the collector tuned circuit L1C1. A very small signal thus develops across L1C1 at the resonant frequency of L2C2. Normal output is obtained at the resonant frequency of L1C1.

Another rejector circuit is shown in Fig. 4.14 in which L1C1 is tuned to the frequency to be rejected.

A complete i.f. strip used in a monochrome receiver is shown in Fig. 4.15. The amplitude-modulated signal is fed into a selective or shaping network before going into a wideband amplifier stage employing integrated circuit MC1352. C4/R7 provides matching between the tuner and the i.f. strip. Network R8/C15/C16/C17/L9 forms a Bridge-T rejector network tuned to the adjacent sound i.f. 41.5 MHz. Capacitor C17 is included to improve the sharpness of the trap, C18/C19/L10 is the adjacent vision trap with L10 tuned to 31.5 MHz and L11 is an interstage coupling coil. Bridge-T rejector C20/C21/L12 provides the necessary 26 dB attenuation for the sound i.f. with L12 tuned to 33.5 MHz. Integrated circuit MC1352 is a wideband i.f. amplifier consisting of a number of amplifying stages which require no tuning. The chip also contains a gain controlled amplifier which is used for automatic gain control purposes (pin 6). The output of the chip (pins 7 and 8) is fed to the detector via top-capacitor coupling unit L13/C33/L14 and diode D2 is a clipping diode which removes the positive half of the modulated i.f.

## Surface acoustic wave filters, SAWF

Increasingly acceptor/rejector type networks are being replaced by surface acoustic wave filters. SAW filters are very reliable, do not require any tuning, are easily serviceable and comparatively cheap. Figure 4.16 shows a section of an i.f. strip in which CF1 is the acoustic surface wave filter which provides all the necessary i.f. selectivity and rejection. Additional gain to compensate for a loss of approximately 20 dB in the SAWF is provided by the wideband amplifying stage VT1/VT2. Resistors R13 and R16 provide negative feedback and L2/C7 is a bandpass filter.

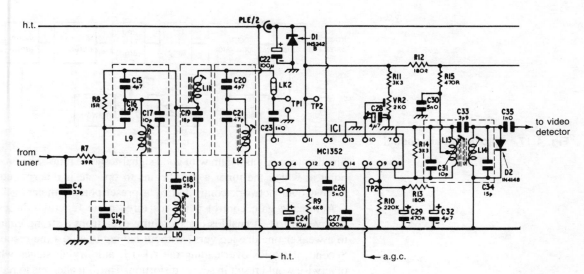

**Fig. 4.15** I.f. strip used in a monochrome receiver (Decca)

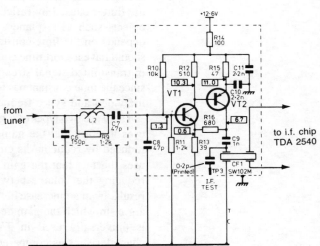

**Fig. 4.16** The use of SAW filter in an i.f. strip (Bush)

## Automatic gain control

The purpose of automatic gain control, a.g.c., is to vary the gain of the i.f. stage and in most cases that of the r.f. amplifier as well to compensate for changes in the strength of the signal received at the aerial. Figure 4.17 shows a block diagram for an a.g.c. system. The strength of the received signal is monitored at the video amplifier stage, fed into an a.g.c. network to produce a d.c. control potential. This voltage is then used to change the gain of the first i.f. stage. The a.g.c. control voltage may also be applied to the tuner in which case a delay unit is employed to ensure that the gain of the r.f. amplifier is reduced only after sufficient reduction of the gain of the i.f. stage has been obtained. With weak signals the r.f. amplifier will thus

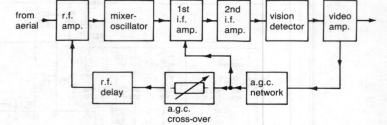

**Fig. 4.17** Automatic gain control

function at maximum gain with good signal-to-noise ratio. The precise point at which the tuner a.g.c. begins to operate is determined by a cross-over network controlled by a preset potentiometer.

Automatic gain control performs three basic functions in a TV receiver. First, it enables the switching over from a strong channel to a weaker one or vice versa without having to adjust the receiver. Second, it avoids overloading the r.f./i.f. amplifying stages which otherwise would result in severe distortion. Third, it attempts to reduce the flutter caused by reflections of transmitted signals from moving objects such as airplanes. The effectiveness of this latter function depends on the time constant of the circuit. Ideally, a.g.c. systems should have a short time constant to enable them to follow fast changes in transmitted signal strength. However, this is not always possible since the time constant has to be long enough to decouple, i.e. remove, the video and sync. frequencies from the d.c. control voltage.

There are two types of a.g.c. — reverse and forward. **Reverse a.g.c.** uses the fact that the gain of a common emitter amplifier may be reduced by reducing its current. **Forward a.g.c.** on the other hand uses the fact that the gain of an amplifier may also be reduced by reducing the voltage between the collector and the emitter which results from an increase in the current through the transistor. Forward a.g.c. in which the gain decreases with increasing transistor current is universally used in TV receivers since it has a more linear characteristics as compared with reverse a.g.c. Furthermore, since weak signals are amplified at low transistor current, it has a better signal-to-noise ratio.

An example of forward a.g.c. is shown in Fig. 4.18 in which R3 is a d.c. load and C1 is its decoupling capacitor. As the transistor current increases, a d.c. voltage develops across R3 which reduces the collector voltage and with it the gain of the amplifier. The decoupling capacitor ensures that the whole signal develops across the tuned circuit L1/C2, and none across R3. The current through the transistor itself is determined by the a.g.c. control potential. An increase in the control voltage results in an increase in the current and hence a reduction in gain and vice versa.

The gain of a tuned amplifier may also be reduced by damping its tuned circuit. In this case a diode is made to conduct when the received signal exceeds a certain level which places a damping resistor across the tuned circuit.

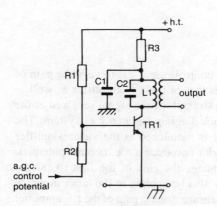

**Fig. 4.18** Principles of forward a.g.c.

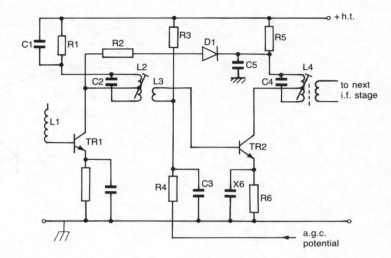

**Fig. 4.19**   Forward a.g.c. circuit

Both forward bias and diode damping may be used simultaneously as shown in Fig. 4.19. With a strong signal the a.g.c. potential is high causing TR2 current to increase, reducing its gain. At the same time, the increase in current causes TR2 collector voltage to decrease which forward biases the damping diode D1. When D1 conducts it places resistor R2 across tuned load L2C2 to further reduce the gain of the i.f. amplifier. Resistor R5 is the d.c. load for TR2 and C5 is its decoupling capacitor. Although R5 is necessary for forward a.g.c., decoupled d.c. load resistors are often incorporated in i.f. amplifiers in order to reduce the d.c. power dissipation of the transistor, e.g. resistor R1 for TR1. Such d.c. loads as R1 do not take part in changing the gain of the transistor since for that to happen the d.c. conditions, i.e. the collector current and voltage, have to change first.

## Peak level a.g.c.

Radio receivers employ what is known as mean level a.g.c. in which the mean level of the received signal is used as a measure of the signal strength. This is unsatisfactory for video reception since the mean level of a video signal does not provide a precise measure of the strength of the signal. As can be seen from Fig. 4.20, the mean value

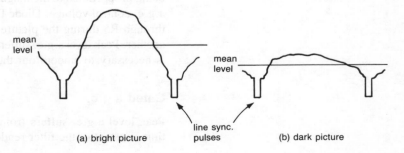

**Fig. 4.20**                                     (a) bright picture                    (b) dark picture

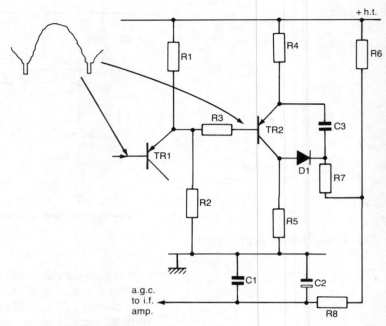

**Fig. 4.21** Peak level a.g.c.

of a video signal reflects the brightness, i.e. luminance content, of the signal. For this reason, peak level (or sync. pulse tip) a.g.c. is employed in which only the peak of the signal, i.e. the tip of the sync. pulses, is monitored. Since the tip of the sync. pulses is always taken to the same level irrespective of the brightness of the picture, then any variation in amplitude reflects the signal strength and nothing else.

Peak level a.g.c. may be obtained by the use of a simple diode (or transistor) clipping circuit to allow only the tips of the sync. pulses through followed by a low pass filter as shown in Fig. 4.21. TR1 is the luminance amplifier acting as an emitter follower feeding the a.g.c. amplifier TR2. Bias chain R1/R2/R3 is arranged to ensure that TR2 is at cut off with its base potential higher than that of the emitter. Since TR2 conducts when its base voltage drops below its emitter potential, then only the most negative parts of the input signal, namely the tips of the line and field sync. pulses, will forward-bias TR2 and make it conduct. The pulses appearing at the output of TR2 are smoothed by low pass filter R7/R8/C2/C1. The charge across C2 being proportional to the magnitude of the sync. pulses, provides the a.g.c. control voltage. Diode D1 ensures that C2 does not discharge through R5 during the picture period between one sync. pulse and another. Peak level a.g.c. suffers from the fact that a long time constant is necessary to smooth out the low frequency 50 Hz field pulses.

## Gated a.g.c.

Peak level a.g.c. suffers from three disadvantages. First, the long time constant of the filter renders the system less sensitive to flutter

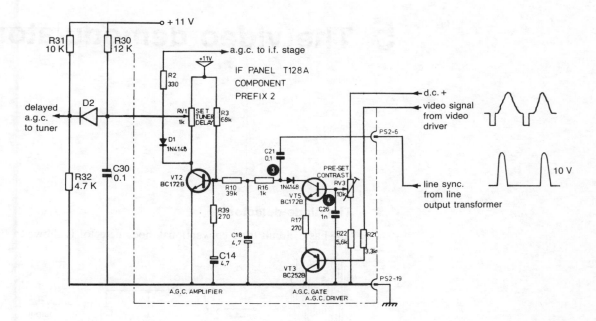

**Fig. 4.22**  Gated a.g.c. circuit in a monochrome receiver (Bush)

in signal strength. Second, it may be rendered ineffective if overloading takes place in any stage before the video amplifier. This is because overloading clips the amplitude of the sync. pulses producing incorrect a.g.c. potential. Third, peak level a.g.c. is susceptible to random noise. The effect of random noise may be removed by the use of a gate which opens only for the duration of the sync. pulses, hence its name **gated a.g.c.** Further improvements may be introduced by gating line sync. pulses only, thus removing the low frequency field pulses making it possible to use a shorter time constant to improve the sensitivity to flutter and other fast changes in signal strength.

A gated a.g.c. circuit used in a monochrome receiver is shown in Fig. 4.22. Transistor VT3 is the a.g.c. gate and VT5 is the a.g.c. driver. VT5 conducts only when a positive-going line pulse coming from the line output transformer is present at its collector. At the same time the negative-going line pulse from the video driver forward biases VT3 making it conduct, enabling an output to appear at the collector of VT5. In this way only the level of the line sync. pulse is monitored. Network R16/C18/R10 is the smoothing filter. The charge on C14 provided by series chain R3/R39 is varied by the level of the incoming sync. pulses. This charge determines the base bias of a.g.c. amplifier VT2 which provides the a.g.c. control voltage for the i.f. stage. Delayed a.g.c. is provided via diode D2 which is turned on when the i.f. stage has reached maximum gain. The cross-over point is set by RV1.

# 5 The video demodulator

### The diode detector

The basic circuit for a conventional diode detector is shown in Fig.

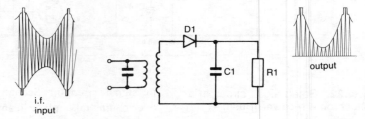

**Fig. 5.1**  Simple diode detector

5.1. It consists of a single rectifier diode D1 shunted by a reservoir capacitor C1 and load resistor R1. The diode conducts for the positive half cycles of the input only. A large input signal is necessary in order to avoid the non-linear part of the diode's transfer characteristics (Fig. 5.2). If the input signal is not large enough distortion is introduced

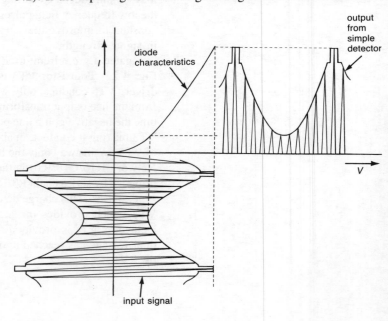

**Fig. 5.2**  Detector diode transfer characteristics

as well as a number of beat frequencies. The values of C1 and R1 are determined by several considerations including the required time constant, the forward resistance and the reverse capacitance of the diode.

## Time constant

For adequate reproduction of the video information, the time constant of the detector, C1R1 must be shorter than the period of one cycle of the highest video frequency, 5.5 MHz, and longer than the duration of one cycle of the 39.5 MHz i.f.

Given that the periodic time of the highest video frequency = 1/5.5 = 0.18 $\mu$s and that of the i.f. = 1/39.5 = 0.025 $\mu$s, the time constant has to be somewhere in between. For this reason 0.1 $\mu$s is normally aimed for. A time constant longer than 0.1 $\mu$s would reduce the high frequency response of the detector. The output which is the charge across C1 is then no longer able to follow the fast changes in brightness which are represented by high video frequencies as shown in Fig. 5.3. On the screen this appears as a smear after a sharp black-to-white edge caused by the inability of the capacitor to discharge quickly. A very short time constant on the other hand would retain a high proportion of the i.f. in the form of a ripple as can be seen in Fig. 5.4.

## The load resistance

The load resistor R1 is required to be as large as possible in order to reduce the relative voltage drop across diode D1 when the latter is forward biased. Given a predetermined time constant of 0.1 $\mu$s, the precise value of the resistor is determined by the minimum value of the capacitance that can be used. The minimum value of the capacitance itself is limited by the reverse capacitance of the diode which allows the i.f. to leak through the output when the diode is not conducting. Capacitor C1 must be large enough to minimise this i.f. leak. Taking all these requirements into consideration, a practical value for the detector load resistor is 5 k$\Omega$.

Detector diodes are chosen to have a low forward voltage drop and hence a low forward resistance and a low reverse capacitance. Germanium diodes are therefore commonly used. The diode is normally provided with a small forward bias to reduce the effect of the non-linearity of its transfer characteristics which is present mainly at low input levels.

As it stands, the output from the basic detector contains a high level of i.f. ripple. This ripple is removed by the introduction of low-pass filter L1C2 (Fig. 5.5). L1 may be tuned with its own self capacitance to 39.5 MHz to provide further rejection of the i.f. ripple. A second inductor L2 is normally added for increased ripple filtering and any other undesirable harmonics. The diode may be reversed to produce

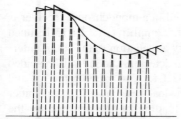

**Fig. 5.3**  Long detector time constant

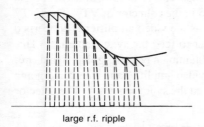

large r.f. ripple

**Fig. 5.4**  Short detector time constant

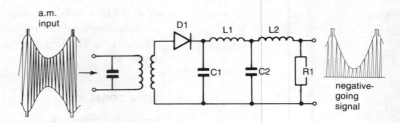

**Fig. 5.5** Diode detector circuit

a positive-going signal. The precise polarity in any one case is determined by the number of phase reversals between the detector and the cathode ray tube. The purpose is to ensure that the cathode of the c.r.t. is ultimately fed with a negative going signal so that peak white corresponds to minimum cathode potential and hence maximum electron emission.

A typical video detector circuit used in a monochrome receiver is shown in Fig. 5.6. VT6 is the last i.f. amplifier, L12/L13 is tuned to 33.5 MHz to provide the necessary attenuation to the sound inter-carrier before feeding the signal to the detector. Diode D4 is the video diode detector with L5/C31/L14/C33/L15/C34 forming the i.f. and harmonics filter network and R31 is the load resistor. VT7 is an emitter follower employed to prevent the loading of the detector by the subsequent low input impedance video amplifier. The emitter follower also serves as a driver for the video amplifier. It is a common technique to use this stage to feed the sync. separator (and sometimes the sound channel) by including resistor R35 in the collector of VT7. Thus VT7 acts as an emitter follower as far as the video amplifier is concerned but as a common emitter amplifier to feed the sync. separator. This is also a convenient method for obtaining a positive-going signal (i.e. negative sync. pulses) to feed the video amplifier and a negative-going signal (positive sync. pulses) to feed the sync. separator. The detector

**Fig. 5.6** Video detector circuit used in monochrome receiver (Bush)

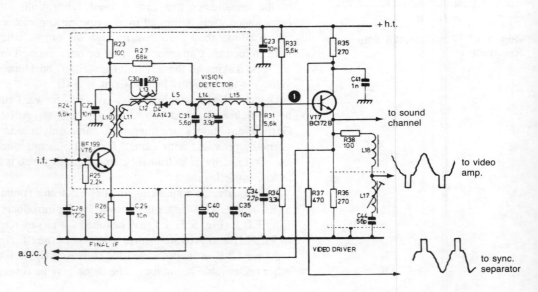

diode is given a small forward bias by resistor R27 going to its anode and potential divider R33/R34 going to the cathode. C35 and C40 are a.g.c. decoupling capacitors.

## Synchronous demodulators

In the amplitude modulated waveform the information is contained in the change of amplitude of the peak of the carrier waveform. By joining the tips of the carrier an envelope is obtained which represents the original modulating information. The purpose of an a.m. demodulator therefore is simply to retrieve that envelope while at the same time removing the carrier wave. This may be carried out by the simple rectifier diode detector. The rectifier is in essence a switch which closes during one half-cycle of the carrier wave and opens during the other half. From this point of view any switching device may be used provided it allows the carrier through for one half cycle only. Since we are only interested in the amplitude of the peak of the carrier, then the switch need only be open for the duration immediately before and immediately after the positive (or negative) peak of the carrier. In truth the modulated carrier is sampled once every cycle of the carrier, a sampling rate equal to the carrier frequency itself.

Figure 5.7 shows a simple block diagram for a synchronous demodulator. The sampling pulses are obtained by the use of a limiter which removes the envelope and leaves a clipped carrier only. The switching or sampling pulses which have the same frequency and the same phase as the carrier are used to control a sampling gate which switches on at the peaks of the modulated carrier. The peak levels are then used to charge a capacitor which, given the correct time constant, will reproduce the original modulating signal. An important characteristic of the synchronous demodulator is that it will only demodulate those a.m. waveforms which have a carrier that is equal in frequency to and is in phase with the sampling pulses.

The output of the synchronous demodulator may be improved by doubling the sampling rate. Two switching square waves in anti-phase to each other are used to operate two separate gates. The two gates are also fed with out-of-phase i.f. signals. The effect is to produce a signal which appears to have passed through a full-wave rectifier. The output contains a carrier component which is twice the frequency of the original carrier making it easy to filter out. Synchronous demodulators are too complex and expensive for construction from discrete components but lend themselves easily for design on a silicon chip as part of an i.f. or video integrated circuit.

Compared with the conventional diode detector, synchronous demodulators have the following advantages:

1.  More linear characteristics.
2.  Low input levels of the order of 50 mV are adequate.
3.  They only detect information modulated on a carrier which

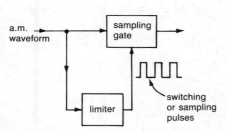

**Fig. 5.7**  Synchronous detector

has the same frequency and phase as the sampling pulses. Any stray modulation caused by noise is therefore removed. Also removed are beat frequencies between the sound i.f. on one hand and the adjacent vision carrier and adjacent sound inter-carrier on the other. Thus, unlike the diode detector which requires a large attenuation (30–40 dB) of the sound i.f., a lower attenuation (20 dB) is adequate for the synchronous demodulator.

4. A simpler RC filter may be used since the ripple has twice the frequency of the ripple produced by the diode detector.

## Practical integrated circuits

Modern i.c.s combine i.f. amplification, vision detection and video driver stages as well as a.g.c. and a.f.c. in a single chip. Figure 5.8 shows a functional diagram of the TBA 440 vision/i.f. chip used in some colour receivers. The i.f. signal is applied to pin 16 via coupling capacitor C314 and fed into a differential amplifier whose gain is controlled by a gated a.g.c. system within the chip. The positive-going video output at pin 11 is taken back to the a.g.c. gate (pin 10) via video level R322 which sets the level of the sync. tips. Gating pulses from the line output stage are applied to pin 7 to trigger the a.g.c.

**Fig. 5.8** TBA 440N vision i.f. chip (ITT)

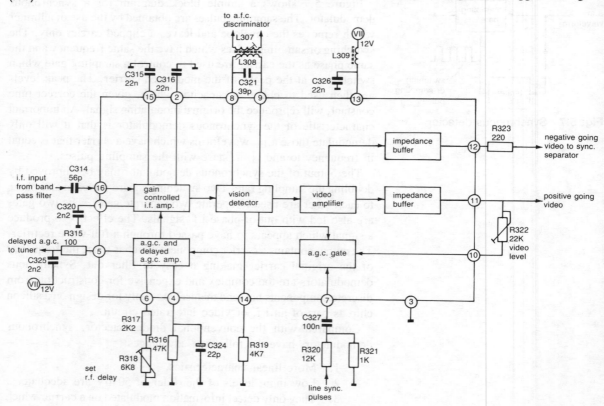

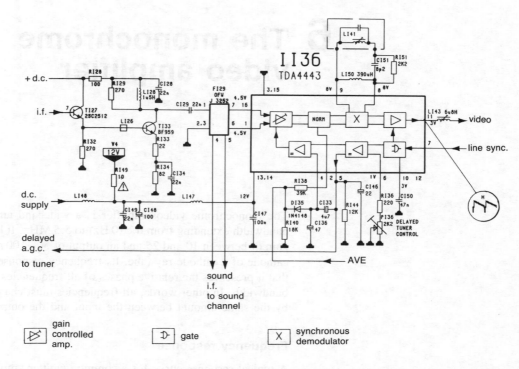

**Fig. 5.9** Vision i.f. circuit using TDA 4443 chip (Ferguson ICC5 colour chassis)

gate whose output is amplified and used to control the gain of the i.f. amplifier and to provide delayed a.g.c. at pin 5. The i.c. contains a synchronous vision detector and a video amplifier. The reference frequency for the synchronous detector is developed across external tuned circuit L308/C321 at pins 8 and 9. The tuned circuit also provides the reference frequency for the a.f.c. discriminator via transformer coupling L308/L307.

A complete vision i.f. circuit using the TDA 4443 chip is shown in Fig. 5.9. The internal arrangements of the chip are shown in symbolic form which today is common to all manufacturers (see Appendix 1). The i.f. signal from the tuner feeds emitter follower TI27 and amplifier TI33 which drives the surface acoustic wave filter F129. The SAW filter has two balanced outputs: one for the vision i.f. and the other for the sound i.f. The vision i.f. signal is applied to i.c. II36 which performs the functions of a.g.c. controlled amplifier, synchronous detector and a.g.c. amplifier. The detector is tuned to 39.5 MHz by external coil LI41 on pins 8 and 9. The tuner a.g.c. is supplied from pin 5 with the cross-over point being adjusted by resistor P136.

# 6 The monochrome video amplifier

The monochrome video amplifier is a wideband amplifier with a bandwidth extending from d.c (0 Hz) to 5.5 MHz. It has a moderate gain of between 10 and 25 and an output of 50−100 mV to feed the cathode of a cathode ray tube. Its frequency response must be such that it preserves the relative phases of all frequencies throughout its bandwidth. In other words, all frequencies must change their phase by the same amount between the input and the output.

## Frequency response

A typical response curve for a common emitter amplifier is shown in Fig. 6.1. The fall at the low frequency end is avoided by direct coupling. The fall at the high-frequency end is more difficult to overcome. The drop in the gain at the upper end is caused by stray capacitors $C_{bc}$ and $C_{ce}$ (Fig. 6.2). The input capacitance $C_i$ of the following stage, namely the tube itself, has a similar effect. These capacitors may be grouped together and represented by a single capacitor $C_t$ falling across the output as shown in Fig. 6.3. The effect of $C_t$ on the gain of the amplifier depends on its reactance $X_t$ which

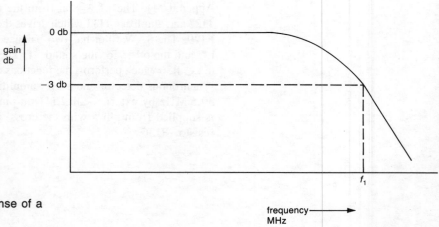

**Fig. 6.1** Frequency response of a common emitter amplifier

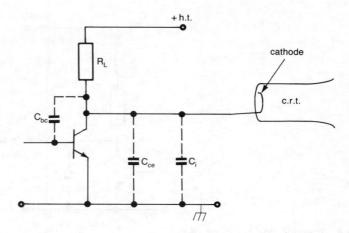

**Fig. 6.2**

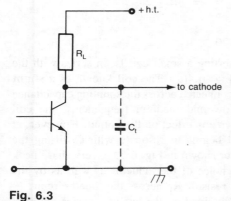

**Fig. 6.3**

varies with the frequency $f$ of the input signal

$$X_t = \frac{1}{2\pi f C_t}$$

At low and medium range frequencies, $X_t$ is large enough to have little or no effect on the gain of the amplifier. As the frequency increases, $X_t$ gets smaller, resulting in a noticeable shunting effect on the output and with it an effect on the gain of the amplifier. At the 3 dB frequency $f_1$ (Fig. 6.1), $X_t = R_L$ and the output power falls to half its midband level. Although transistors with high cut-off frequencies may be employed, the video bandwidth cannot be fully accommodated without some form of compensatory network to overcome the fall at the high-frequency end. There are three commonly used high-frequency compensation techniques.

### Small $R_L$ compensation

If a small load resistor $R_L$ is used then the 3 dB frequency $f_1$ increases, extending the bandwidth of the amplifier. However this method is of limited use since it also increases the power dissipation of the transistor:

> Power dissipation = d.c input power − a.c. (or signal) output power

Given that

> d.c. input = $I_c \times$ h.t.

where $I_c$ is the collector current and h.t. is the d.c. supply, then a change in $R_L$ has no effect on $I_c$ keeping the d.c. power unchanged. However, a reduction in the load resistor will reduce the a.c. signal power output with a consequent increase in the power dissipation of the transistor.

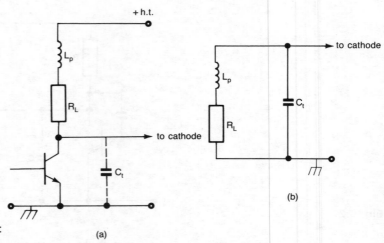

**Fig. 6.4** Peaking coil compensation:
(a) circuit, (b) effective tuned circuit

## Peaking coil compensation

This technique involves inserting a small coil $L_p$ in series with the load resistor as shown in Fig. 6.4(a). The coil known as a **shunt peaking** coil, is effectively connected across the shunting capacitance $C_t$ as shown in (b). At low and medium frequencies, the coil reactance is too small to have any effect on the output. However, at higher frequencies the coil begins to resonate with $C_t$ lifting the response curve in the manner shown in Fig. 6.5. A very sharp peak is avoided by the suitable choice of the inductor as well as by the damping effect of the load resistor $R_L$ across the tuned circuit.

A similar effect may be obtained by the use of a **series peaking** coil $L_s$ (Fig. 6.6). In this case, the peaking coil separates the total shunting capacitor roughly into two parts: C1 representing the transistor stray capacitors and C2 representing the c.r.t input capacitance. C1/$L_s$/C2 functions as a low pass filter which may be

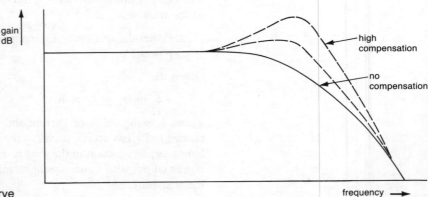

**Fig. 6.5** Effect of frequency
compenstion on response curve

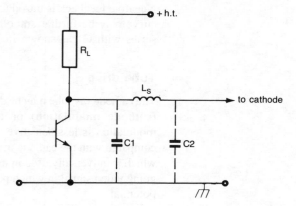

**Fig. 6.6**  Series peaking coil

designed to lift the high frequency end in a similar way to the shunt peaking coil.

In many application both shunt and series peaking are employed to provide a smooth high-frequency response.

### Frequency selective negative feedback

The basic principle behind this technique is to arrange for the negative feedback produced by the emitter resistor to be removed gradually as the frequency approaches the high end of the response curve. It involves selecting an emitter decoupling capacitor which does not provide adequate decoupling at low and midband frequencies. Partial decoupling is very simple and extremely popular. However, it does involve a reduction in the overall gain of the amplifier.

In Fig. 6.7(a) the decoupling capacitor C1 is chosen to have a small value (820 pF instead of the normal 100 $\mu$F). At high-frequencies the reactance of C1 is very low compared with emitter resistor R1. Negative feedback is therefore removed and the gain is high. At low frequencies, C1 reactance increases reducing its decoupling effect.

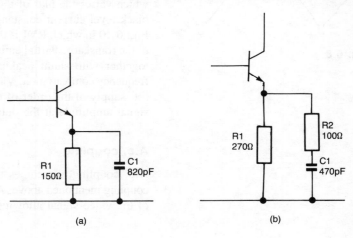

**Fig. 6.7**  Frequency selective decoupling

(a)                                         (b)

Negative feedback is introduced which lowers the gain. The response curve may be further smoothed by the addition of a resistor R2 in series with C1 as shown in Fig. 6.7(b).

## Tube drive

The cathode ray tube may be driven by a video signal fed to the cathode (**cathode modulation**) or to the grid (**grid modulation**). Grid modulation is less sensitive and thus requires a larger video signal compared with the cathode modulation technique. Cathode modulation which is universally used in modern TV receivers requires a negative-going video signal in which peak white represents a minimum cathode potential.

## Direct video coupling

In order to produce a negative-going signal at the output of the amplifier it has to be fed with a positive-going signal. The positive-going input is produced by detecting the negative half of the modulated i.f. as shown in Fig. 6.8. As can be seen, the detected signal is wholly negative with peak white at a maximum or zero volts. If this signal is directly coupled to the video amplifier, a large positive bias is necessary to ensure that the transistor conducts while the amplitude is above the black level with a maximum current at peak white. This is illustrated in Fig. 6.9(a) in which $I_{b1}$ is the necessary bias current. This arrangement is very wasteful in h.t. supply current and expensive in terms of power dissipation and the working life of the transistor since even with no signal present the transistor continues to take maximum current. Direct coupling suffers from another disadvantage: low signal amplitudes caused by reducing the contrast result in the transistor conducting as shown in Fig. 6.9(b). While peak white is still represented by maximum current, black level current is increased. This second disadvantage may be overcome by using a contrast control which varies the bias of the transistor in such a way as to keep the black level current constant. A typical video amplifier is shown in Fig. 6.10 in which RV1 is the contrast control which defines the bias of the transistor. Partial emitter decoupling R4/C1 is employed which together with shunt peaking coil L1 provides the necessary high frequency compensation. Video amplifiers have to employ an auxiliary h.t. supply of the order of 60−100 V to provide the necessary high signal amplitude at the output.

## A.c. coupling

A.c. coupling overcomes the disadvantages associated with direct coupling mentioned above. A.c. coupling removes the d.c. component of the video signal allowing the transistor to be biased in Class A,

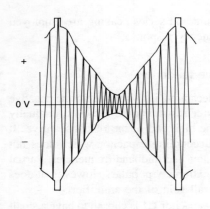

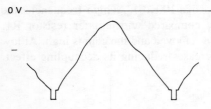

**Fig. 6.8**

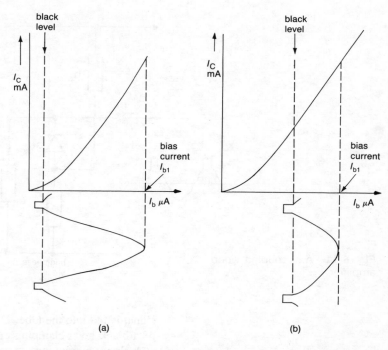

**Fig. 6.9**                                    (a)                                    (b)

i.e. in the middle of its characteristics. The time constant introduced by the coupling capacitor may seem to be a disadvantage in terms of the low-frequency response of the amplifier. However, the time constant may be used to reduce the effect of flutter on the signal. The d.c. component of the video signal which represents the average brightness of the picture and therefore must be restored before the

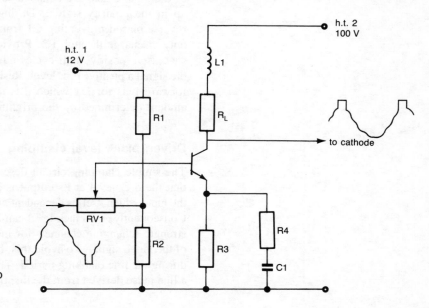

**Fig. 6.10**  Directly coupled video amplifier

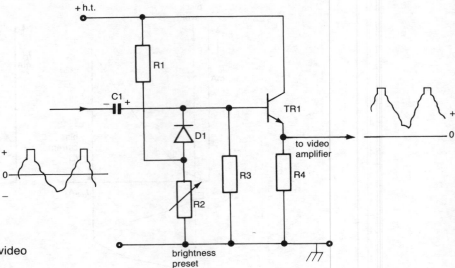

**Fig. 6.11** A.c. coupled video amplifier

signal is fed into the tube. D.c. restoration is carried out by the use of a black level clamping circuit.

A circuit employing a.c. coupling is shown in Fig. 6.11 in which TR1 is the emitter follower stage between the detector and the video amplifier. C1 couples the video signal from the vision detector to the base of the video amplifier TR1. D1 is the clamping diode and the d.c. clamping level is determined by the setting of R2. The operation of the clamper is based on the fact that during the negative half cycles of the input signal D1 conducts and coupling capacitor C1 charges up in the polarity shown. During the positive half-cycles, D1 is reverse-biased preventing C1 from discharging through R2. It can only discharge through R3. Provided time constant C1R3 is large, successive positive half-cycles build up a charge across C1 giving the signal a positive d.c. level. Resistor chain R1/R2 provides a small forward bias for D1 which lifts the video signal above 0 V by an amount determined by the brightness preset resistor R2.

### Driven black level clamping

The simple clamping circuit described above suffers from the fact that the d.c. level at its output is determined by the mean value of the input which itself is dependent on the amplitude of the video signal. Consequently, the black level can be affected by variations in signal strength (changing channels for instance) as well as by the contents of the video signal. To avoid this, black level clamping is carried out during the line blanking period. The clamping circuits are driven by a line pulse derived from the line timebase. In this way the d.c. level

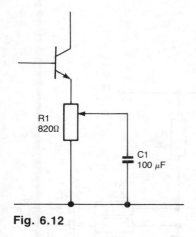

**Fig. 6.12**

is set at the start of each active picture line and, provided the time constant is comparatively long, it remains constant throughout regardless of the contents of the signal. Driven black level clamping is essential for colour receivers where three independent signals, red, green and blue, are used to drive the three cathodes of a colour tube.

### Contrast control

The contrast of a picture on the c.r.t. screen may be varied by varying the a.g.c. voltage as was explained in Chapter 4. This method involves changing the gain of the i.f/video stages and hence it is only included as a preset contrast control. The variable contrast control available to the user is obtained by varying the amplitude of the signal fed into the tube. This may be carried out by inserting a variable resistor RV1 in series with the input to the video amplifier as was illustrated in Fig. 6.10. A second technique is to vary the amount of emitter decoupling (Fig. 6.12) in which full decoupling is obtained when the slider is moved to the top end of variable resistor R1 to provide maximum gain, maximum output and hence maximum contrast. As the slider moves towards the chassis, the decoupling effect of C1 diminishes to introduce negative feedback, low gain, low output and low contrast.

### Protection against flash-over

The build-up of high voltages inside the tube sometimes results in flash-over between the electrodes. This is most likely to happen in colour TV display tubes where voltages of up to 25 kV are used. The large transient current resulting from such a flash-over may damage the circuit components outside the c.r.t. To protect the external circuitry, capacitors or sparking gaps are connected between high voltage electrodes such as the first anode or the focus electrodes and earth to bypass any transient current.

### Flyback blanking

Ideally the line and field flyback lines should occur below the black level of the video signal so that they are not visible on the screen. However, under certain conditions such as excessive brightness, the flyback trace may become visible and has to be suppressed. Flyback suppression is obtained by turning off the c.r.t. for the duration of the line and field flyback. This is called **flyback blanking**. The simplest blanking technique is to feed a negative-going line and field sync. pulse from the line and field timebases into the first grid of the c.r.t. to turn the tube off. A second method is to feed the sync. pulses into the video amplifier to turn the transistor off and ensure a black level potential at the cathode of the c.r.t. for the duration of the flyback

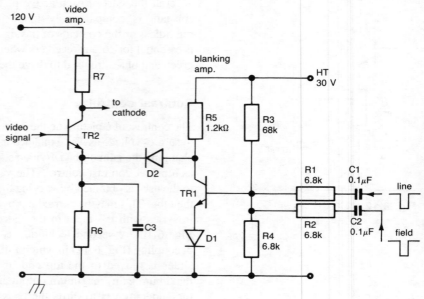

**Fig. 6.13** Flyback blanking circuit

as shown in Fig. 6.13. Negative-going line and field sync. pulses are fed via R1/C1 and R2/C2 respectively to the base of blanking amplifier TR1. Transistor TR1 is biased at saturation with its collector at very low potential (about 1 V) which is lower than the potential of TR2 emitter. Diode D2 is therefore reverse-biased acting as an open circuit. When a sync. pulse arrives, TR1 base voltage is brought down turning the transistor off. The collector of TR1 goes up to HT and D2 conducts to feed a positive-going pulse into the emitter of video amplifier TR2. For the duration of the pulse, the potential of TR2 emitter remains higher than its base, keeping TR2 off with its collector (and c.r.t. cathode) at 120 V h.t. potential. The tube is therefore blanked.

## Beam current limiting

Changes in the tube beam current between the cathode and the final anode caused by changes in brightness can cause the e.h.t. voltage supply to the final anode to vary. The e.h.t. is regulated up to a maximum beam current which when exceeded causes changes in brightness and variations in picture size. To prevent this, a beam limiter is used. For a monochrome receiver, the limiter is normally a simple diode connected between the video amplifier and the c.r.t. as shown in Fig. 6.14. Under normal conditions, D1 conducts providing direct coupling between video amplifier TR1 and the cathode of the c.r.t. Beam current $I_B$ flows into the cathode of the c.r.t. via the parallel paths TR1/D1 and R2 as shown. The voltage developed across R2 is small enough to keep D1 forward biased. When the beam

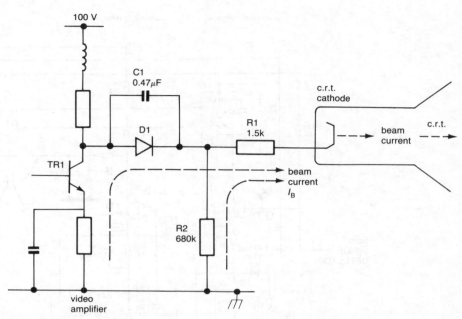

**Fig. 6.14**  Beam current limiting. D1 is the limiter diode

current exceeds a certain level, say $100\,\mu A$, the voltage across R2 is high enough to cause D1 to become reverse-biased thus removing the d.c. coupling. The beam now flows solely through R2 causing its voltage drop to rise. This rise in the potential of the cathode reduces the effective cathode–anode voltage and with it the beam current. The video signal is now a.c. coupled via capacitor C1 which removes the black level set by TR1 collector voltage.

## Typical video stages

A typical video stage for a monochrome receiver is shown in Fig. 6.15. Transistors VT5 and VT7 are the emitter follower video driver and the video output amplifier respectively. The video signal taken from the emitter of VT5 is fed directly to the base of VT7. The same signal is also fed to the sync. separator. The 6 MHz sound inter-carrier is taken off at the collector of VT5 using the parallel tuned transformer L10/C43 with R60 as the damping resistor. Resistor R24 together with the d.c. voltage from the diode detector (not shown) provides the bias voltage for VT5. The 6 MHz rejection is provided by L9/C46 and bandwidth extension is provided by selective decoupling capacitors C47 and C48. Contrast control is provided by the partial decoupling of the emitter of VT7. Flyback blanking is obtained by feeding the sync. pulses into the emitter of VT7 to turn the amplifier off during flyback. The line sync. pulses are also fed into the a.g.c. gate transistor VT6 via diode W3. The a.g.c. level is varied by R32 to provide a

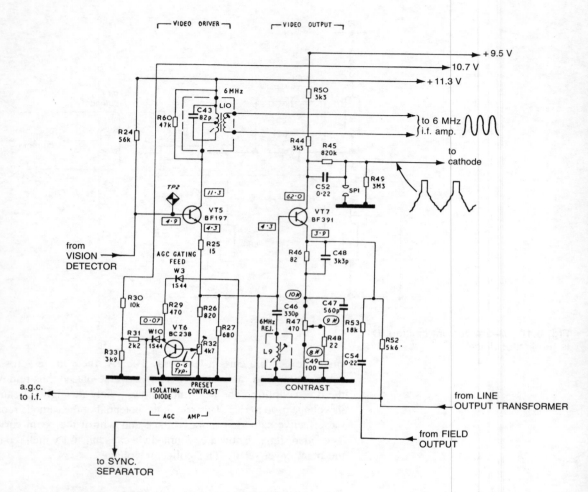

**Fig. 6.15** Monochrome video stage (Ferguson 1690 chassis)

preset contrast control. Sparking gap SP1 protects the video amplifier against flash-over in the tube. The output from VT7 is fed to the cathode of the c.r.t. via time constant R45/C52 which limits the response of the tube to flutter.

Another video output stage is shown in Fig. 6.16 in which TR351 is the video driver, TR353 is the video output, TR352 is the blanking amplifier, C204 is the coupling capacitor, D351 is the video clamp diode and P351 is the black level control. Blanking amplifier TR352 is switched on by positive-going sync. pulses into its base which then shorts out the base of the video amplifier, turns TR353 off and blanks the tube. Frequency selective feedback is provided by C352/R358/R359 to improve the frequency response. L351/C353 is a colour subcarrier trap tuned to 4.43 MHz. Its purpose is to remove the subcarrier used in colour transmissions. D352 and its associated C351 and R357 form a beam limiter circuit.

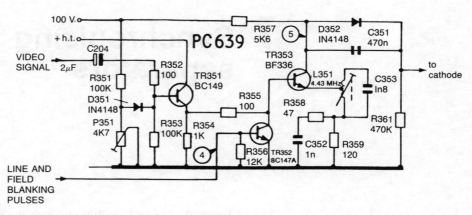

**Fig. 6.16**  Monchrome video stage
(GEC)

# 7 Synchronising separators

The purpose of the synchronising separator is to slice the sync. pulses off the composite video waveform, separate them into line and field and feed each one to the appropriate timebase. The process must be immune to changes in the amplitude and picture composition of the video signal.

It may be recalled that the sync. pulses are arranged to fall beyond the black level and to occupy 30% of the total amplitude of the composite video. A clipping network is therefore all that is required in order to separate the sync. pulses away from the video information.

A simple sync. separator is shown in Fig. 7.1. Capacitor C1 ensures that TR1 is biased in class C, i.e. beyond cut off. Without an input, TR1 base is at zero potential. When an input signal is applied to coupling capacitor C1, the positive part of the signal makes the base—emitter, b—e, junction conduct. The resulting b—e current charges C1 in such a way as to make the base go negative. Because of the relatively long time constant of C1R1, the capacitor retains the charge thus providing a reverse bias (class C) for TR1 which is dependent on the amplitude of the input signal. With class C biasing the transistor will only conduct and produce an output at its collector when the signal input is high enough to overcome the reverse bias. This condition

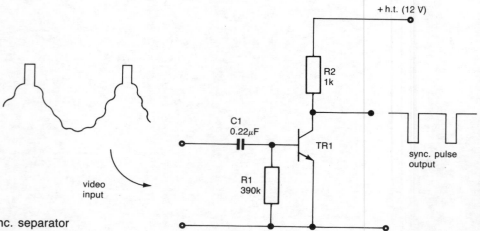

**Fig. 7.1**  Simple sync. separator

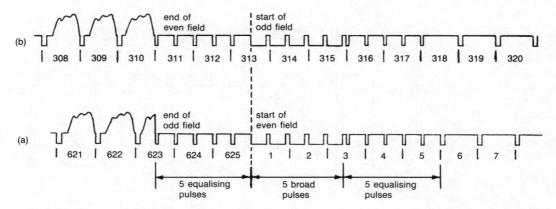

**Fig. 7.2** Field broad pulses: (a) odd field, (b) even field

is satisfied by the positive tips of the sync. pulses. The video information falling below this level will therefore be removed.

Once the sync. pulses have been separated from the composite video, the receiver must be able to distinguish between the two types of sync. pulses. This distinction is effected by sending the field sync. pulses in the form of a pulse-width modulated waveform consisting of five consecutive broad pulses at twice line frequency as shown in Fig. 7.2. The field flyback lasts for 25 complete lines giving a total field blanking time of $25 \times 64 = 1600\,\mu s$. In order to ensure continuous line synchronisation throughout the field blanking period, it is necessary for line triggering edges to occur where a line sync. pulse normally appears. The twice-line frequency broad pulses ensure that this takes place. The extra edges during the field flyback are disregarded by the line oscillator. Before and after the five broad field pulses, five equalising pulses are inserted for the purpose of ensuring good interlacing.

### The integrator method

A common method of separating the line from the field sync. pulses is the use of an integrator (Fig. 7.3). The time constant CR is chosen to be longer than the duration of a line sync. pulse but slightly shorter than the duration of a complete line, something in the region of $50\,\mu s$. The effect of such an integrator on the sync. pulses is illustrated in

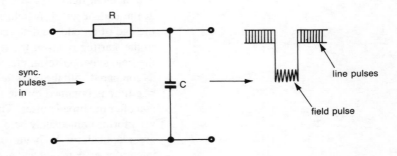

**Fig. 7.3** Integrator method

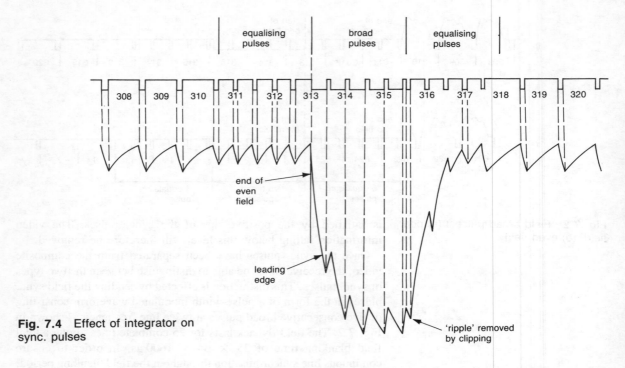

**Fig. 7.4** Effect of integrator on sync. pulses

Fig. 7.4. The capacitor charges up during the presence of a pulse and discharges when the pulse is absent. The charge developed across C during a narrow line pulse is small and the capacitor is fully discharged by the time the next line pulse arrives. For the field pulses, the capacitor charging time is long while its discharging time is short. A charge thus accumulates across the capacitor as one broad pulse follows another, lifting the field pulses above the line sync. pulses as shown. At the end of the five broad pulses, the capacitor discharges gradually during the equalising pulses. A rising leading edge is thus produced which is subsequently clipped thus removing the 'ripple' present at its tip to obtain the field sync. pulse.

## Equalising pulses

Interlacing involves the scanning of two separate fields: an odd field and an even field. The two fields are not identical since the flyback at the end of an even field starts at the end of a line while that at the end of an odd field starts in the middle of a line. The difference in the starting point of the flyback produces a different rise time in the field sync. pulses at the output of the integrator for the odd fields as compared with the even fields, resulting in bad interlacing. Identical rise time is obtained by the introduction of equalising pulses before and after the broad pulses. The equalising pulses ensure that the pulse waveforms immediately before and immediately after the broad pulses are identical for both the odd and even fields. The effect of the integrator on both odd and even fields is shown in Fig. 7.5. Occurring

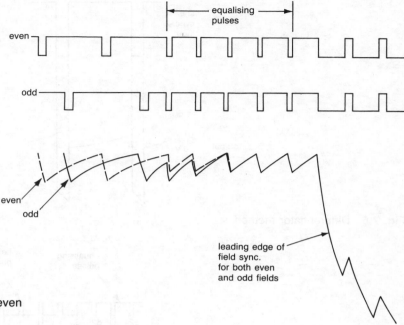

**Fig. 7.5** Effect of integrator on even and odd fields

at twice the line frequency, the equalising pulses coincide with an end of line for the even field and the middle of a line for an odd field producing identical rise time for both fields and identical flyback.

The field sync. pulse produced by the integrator does not have a very sharp edge. The sharpness of the edge may be improved by amplification and clipping. However, the slow response is an advantage in that it reduces the effect of stray or random transient pulses which tend to disturb the field synchronisation resulting in jitter in the picture on the screen.

## Differentiator method

A very sharp pulse may be produced by the use of a differentiator. Given a time constant of the same order as the period of the input waveform, the output of a differentiator is of the same shape as the input but with a different d.c. level. Figure 7.6(a) shows the output waveform when the input to the differentiator has a high mark-to-space ratio, i.e. a negative-going narrow pulse similar to a line sync. pulse. Figure 7.6(b) shows the effect on the output when the input mark-to-space ratio is reduced to a value much smaller than one, i.e. a positive-going narrow pulse similar to a broad field pulse. In the first case, the output pulse is negative while in the second it is positive. In this way the field broad pulses may be lifted above the line sync. pulses as shown in Fig. 7.7. The output is clipped to remove variation in amplitude and to provide a sharp triggering edge. Once again the equalising pulses ensure identical field pulses for both even and odd fields.

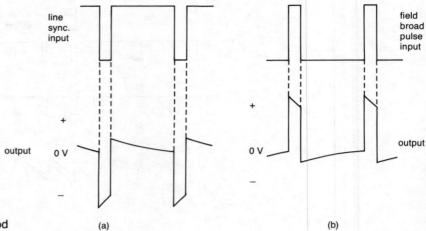

**Fig. 7.6** Differentiator method

(a)

(b)

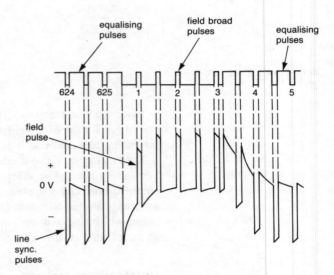

**Fig. 7.7** Effect of differentiator on sync. pulses

## A typical sync. separator circuit

A typical sync. separator is shown in Fig. 7.8 in which TR5 is the sync. separator transistor biased in class C by coupling capacitor C47. The reverse bias of $-0.68$ V is determined by resistor R35. Negative-going line and field sync. pulses are produced at the collector of TR5. The line pulses are differentiated by C81 before going to the line timebase. The field pulses are integrated by R39/C49 and clipped by D4 before going to the field timebase. TR5 has a high cut-off frequency in order to maintain the sharp triggering edges of the output.

## Noise

Random pulses due to noise and other interference are sometimes present on the composite video signal. These pulses are similar to

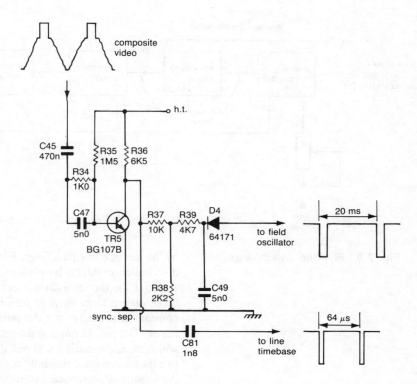

**Fig. 7.8** Sync. separator circuit (Decca)

the sync. pulses themselves and may trigger the timebase at the wrong time. In the case of the field timebase, the integrator which has a slow response removes most of the noise. However, a random pulse occurring near the end of a field causes what is known as frame or **field slip**. To avoid this, a noise gate (also known as a noise canceller) may be included to obtain a noise-free output from the sync. separator.

In the case of the line timebase, noise causes what is known as **line tearing** as some lines are displaced with respect to the others. On vertical objects, the effect of line tearing is illustrated by ragged edges. Line tearing may be avoided by the use of a flywheel synchronising circuit. The principle of flywheel synchronisation is similar to that of the mechanical flywheel which, due to its large momentum maintains an average speed unaffected by random changes. The flywheel sync. circuit maintains an average frequency of the sync. pulses by monitoring and taking the average frequency of a number of incoming line pulses so that a random pulse will have very little effect on the frequency.

A block diagram for a flywheel synchroniser is shown in Fig. 7.9. It consists of a flywheel discriminator followed by a reactance stage which controls the frequency of the line oscillator. The flywheel discriminator itself consists of a phase comparator or discriminator and a smoothing circuit. A control voltage proportional to the timing, i.e. phase, between the line oscillator and the incoming sync. pulse is obtained from the phase comparator. The voltage is then smoothed

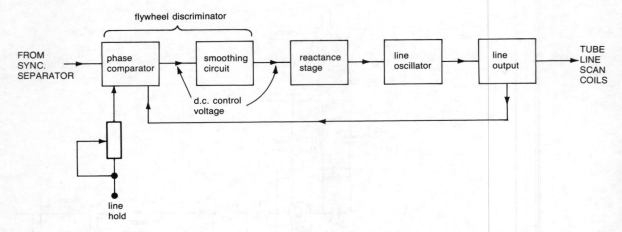

**Fig. 7.9** Flywheel synchroniser

by the use of a low pass filter. For good noise immunity the flywheel discriminator should have slow response which means a long time constant for the smoothing circuit so that the average frequency is taken over a large number of line sync. pulses. However, the time constant also determines the **pull-in range** of the flywheel discriminator. The pull-in range is the range of oscillator frequency drift over which the discriminator will pull the oscillator into lock without having to adjust the manual line hold control. A short time constant improves the sensitivity and hence widens the pull-in range of the discriminator. A compromise has to be struck with the oscillator designed to have stability within the pull-in range of the discriminator.

## The flywheel discriminator

A simplified circuit of a flywheel discriminator is shown in Fig. 7.10 in which C4/R4 is a smoothing circuit. Line sync. pulses from the line output transformer are integrated by R1/C1 and the resulting reference sawtooth waveform is fed via C2 into the phase comparator D1/D2. At the same time negative-going sync. pulses from the sync. separator are fed into the comparator at the cathodes of D1 and D2 pulsing the two diodes into conduction and clamping the reference sawtooth waveform for the duration of the line pulse.

If the line oscillator is running at the correct speed, both the sync. pulse and the sawtooth reference signal will coincide in such a way as to clamp the sawtooth waveform at zero volts (point A in Fig. 7.11). D1 and D2 conduct equally with the two currents $I_1$ and $I_2$ cancelling each other and producing a zero d.c. output.

If the oscillator is running fast, the sawtooth waveform has a higher frequency and hence a shorter periodic time. In this case the sync. pulse will coincide with the negative voltage part of the sawtooth waveform causing D2 to conduct. A negative d.c. voltage is thus obtained at the output. Conversely, if the oscillator was running slow, the sync. pulse would coincide with the positive part of the sawtooth

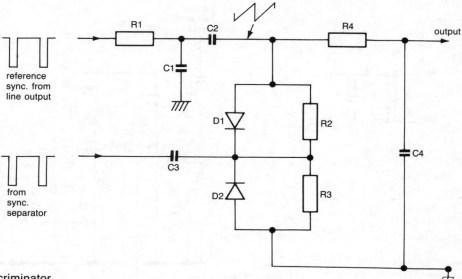

**Fig. 7.10** Flywheel discriminator

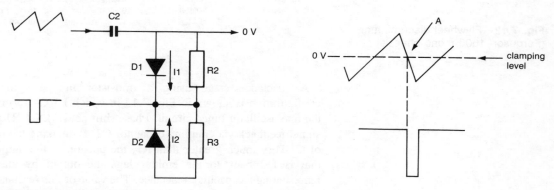

**Fig. 7.11** Flywheel discriminator with line oscillator running at correct speed

waveform causing D1 to conduct producing a positive d.c. output.

A flywheel discriminator circuit employing a phase splitter is shown in Fig. 7.12. The line sync. pulses from sync. separator VT9 are fed into phase splitter VT12 via differentiator C106/R118. The two anti-phase sync. pulses M1 and M2 are then fed into the flywheel discriminator pulsing W25 and W26 into conduction and clamping the sawtooth reference waveform at the junction of the two diodes in the same manner as described earlier. C109 is part of the smoothing network which feeds the d.c. control voltage to the reactance stage.

## The reactance stage

The purpose of the reactance stage is to convert a variation in the d.c. control voltage into a variation of reactance. A varactor is commonly employed although bipolar and unipolar transistors may also be used.

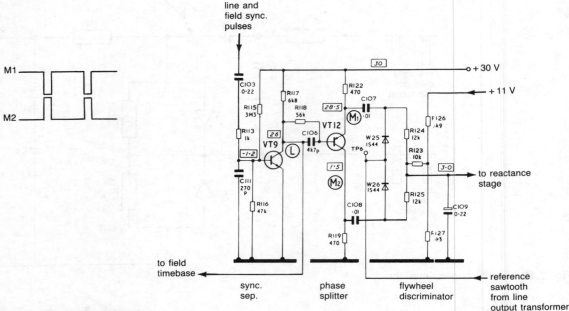

**Fig. 7.12** Flywheel discriminator (Ferguson 1600 mono chassis)

A reactance stage using a transistor in the common-base configuration is shown in Fig. 7.13 in which L1/C4 forms part of the line oscillator tuned circuit. Phase shift network C1/R1 provides signal feedback via coupling capacitor C2. By making the reactance of C1 very much greater than R1, the portion of the output signal that is fed back to the emitter lags the output by almost 90° representing a capacitive reactance. The value of this reactance which effectively falls across L1/C1 is determined by the operating point of the transistor which may be varied by the d.c. control voltage going into the base.

## Stability of line flyback pulses

The stability of the line flyback pulses is important in order to ensure a stable picture. For colour receivers, it is critical since the line sync. pulses are used to perform a number of gating functions in the colour decoder.

Although the line oscillator is locked by the flywheel sychronising circuit, problems of the stability of the line flyback are by no means completely resolved. This is because the line output stage which utilises the line flyback to generate the e.h.t. has to supply a continuously varying tube beam current. The beam current varies as the brightness along the scan line changes, which in turn varies the demand made on the line output stage causing the timing of the line

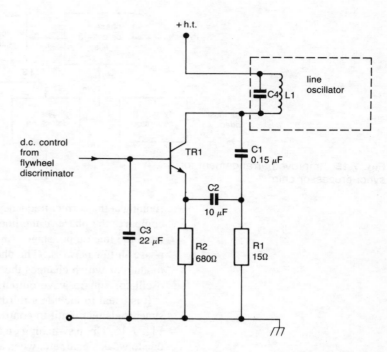

**Fig. 7.13** Reactance stage

flyback to change. The stability of the line flyback may be greatly improved by the use of integrated circuits which employ a more accurate flywheel synchronising system.

### Sync. processing chips

Figure 7.14 shows the basic arrangement of an i.c. sync. processing system in which phase-locked loops act as flywheel synchronisers. The stability of the line flyback is secured by the use of two phase-locked loops, PLL1 and PLL2. Phase detector 1 compares the phase of the square wave output of the line oscillator with the line sync. from the sync. separator and so ensures that the line oscillator is

**Fig. 7.14** Basic arrangement for a sync. processing chip

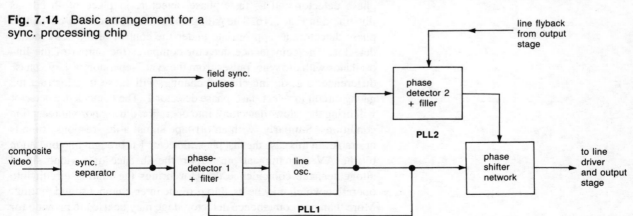

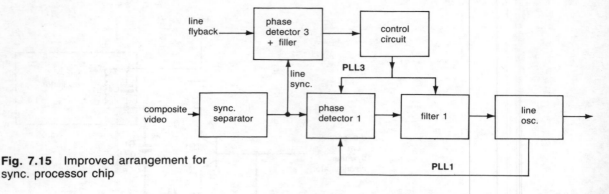

**Fig. 7.15** Improved arrangement for sync. processor chip

running at the correct frequency and phase. The second phase detector compares the phase of the line oscillator with the line flyback pulse from the line output stage. Any phase error is then corrected by the phase shifter network. The phase shifter is in essence a pulse-width modulator which changes the width and hence the phase of the line oscillator square wave output.

It is usual to include a third phase-locked loop, PLL3, in the line synchronising circuit to control the sensitivity of PLL1 as shown in Fig. 7.15. Upon switching on or on changing channels or at any time due to weak signal, etc. when a momentary loss of line oscillator lock occurs, it is desirable for PLL1 to have a fast response, i.e. low phase detector sensitivity and a short filter time constant so that good 'pull-in' and hence quick lock is obtained. Once the oscillator has been brought into lock, a slow response is desirable, i.e. high sensitivity and a long time constant to improve the accuracy of the oscillator and improve the discrimination of the system against noise and interference. To do this, phase detector 3 is used which compares the phase of the line flyback from the line output stage with the sync. pulse from the sync. separator. An output is produced when the two pulses are in phase, in which case the control circuit changes the sensitivity of PLL1 and the time constant of filter 1.

Some integrated circuits employ two phase-locked loops, a 'slow' phase detector and a 'fast' phase detector, in place of PLL1, as illustrated in Fig. 7.16. The gating circuit then selects one of the two phase detectors as appropriate under the control of the coincidence detector. The coincidence detector compares the output of the line oscillator with the sync. pulses from the sync. separator. A large phase difference, e.g. during channel change, will cause it to instruct the gating circuit to select 'fast' phase detector 1. The coincidence detector will bring the 'slow' detector 2 into operation during normal reception conditions. Similarly, with an off-tape signal a fast response time is desirable. In this case the fast phase detector 1 is brought into operation by the AV switching at pin 18. In the absence of a video signal altogether, the coincidence detector brings the muting circuit into operation which may be used to provide inter-channel sound muting. More than one coincidence detector stage may be used to provide for

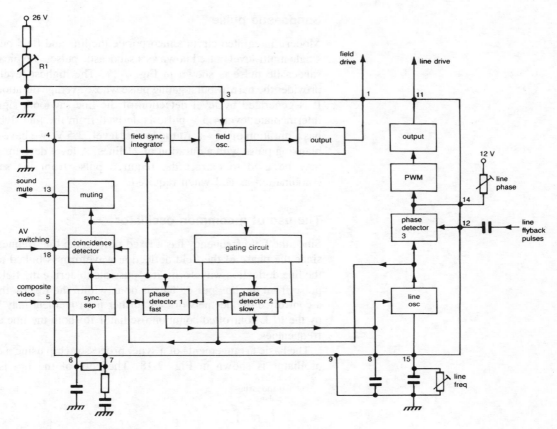

**Fig. 7.16**  Basic components of a practical sync. processor (TDA 4578 part)

more than two possible levels of sensitivity of the line sync. system. Optimum sensitivity may then be selected depending on the strength of the received signal. The field sync. pulses from the separator are integrated and used to trigger the field oscillator whose frequency is set by R1 (pin 3). The sawtooth waveform thus produced then appears at pin 1 to be used to drive the field output stage.

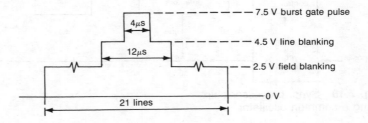

**Fig. 7.17**  Sandcastle pulse

## Sandcastle pulse

Modern integrated circuits incorporate the line and field pulses in a single multi-level pulse known as a sandcastle pulse. A typical 3-level sandcastle pulse is shown in Fig. 7.17. The highest level, 7.5 V, provides the narrow burst gating pulse whose average duration is 4 $\mu$s. It is generated by level detection of the line sawtooth signal. The intermediate level 4.5 V pulse is derived from the line flyback and has a duration of 12 $\mu$s. At the lowest level, 2.5 V, we have the field blanking pulse with a duration of 21 lines. A level detector or slicer may be used to extract the required pulse from the sandcastle combination as and when required.

## The use of a common oscillator

Since the field frequency has a fixed ratio to the line frequency, and since the phase of the field deflection waveform is linked to that of the line deflection waveform, it is possible to derive the field trigger pulse from the line pulse. This is done within the i.c. by the use of a controlled divider network. A further improvement may be made by the PLL controlled common oscillator for both the line and field frequencies.

The basic arrangements of a sync. processor chip using a common oscillator is shown in Fig. 7.18. The core of the i.c. is a PLL

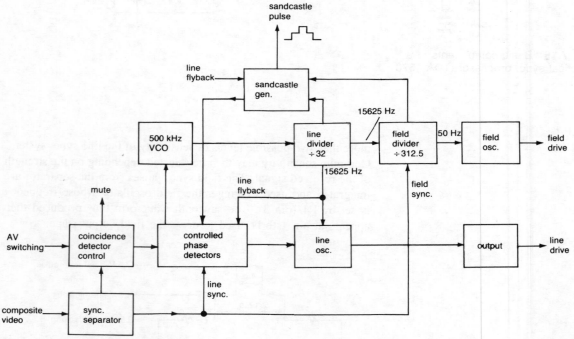

**Fig. 7.18** Sync. processor chip using a common oscillator

controlled VCO which oscillates at 500 kHz. The output of the oscillator is divided by 32 (line divider) to give a line scan frequency of 15 625 Hz. Line synchronisation is provided by a multi-stage controlled phase detector which compares the phases of the line pulse from the divider and the flyback from the line output stage with the sync. pulse to control the phase and frequency of the VCO and trigger the line oscillator. Field frequency is obtained by dividing the line frequency by 312.5 (field divider). The divider is controlled by the sync. pulses from the sync. separator to set the phase of the field signal correctly. The line, field and flyback pulses are built-up into a sandcastle pulse by the sandcastle generator as shown.

# 8 Field timebase

The field timebase in a TV receiver consists of a sawtooth generator followed by a driver and an output stage which feeds the field scan coils. The sawtooth generator contains a free running pulse oscillator which is triggered by the field sync. pulse derived from the sync. separator. The oscillator includes a facility for manual control of its frequency for 'field hold' as well as one or more controls to ensure vertical linearity.

## Sawtooth generation

Sawtooth generation is obtained by charging and discharging a capacitor as shown in Fig. 8.1(a) in which TR1 forms part of the field oscillator circuit. When TR1 is switched off, capacitor C1 charges up slowly (scan) through R1 and towards h.t.. Well before the capacitor voltage reaches h.t., a positive-going field sync. pulse arrives at the base turning the transistor on and discharging the capacitor very quickly to zero (flyback). The capacitor remains discharged for the duration of the input pulse. When the pulse comes to an end TR1 is switched off and the capacitor begins to charge up, and so on. The result is the sawtooth waveform shown in Fig. 8.1(b). The frequency of the waveform is the same as that of the input pulse while its amplitude is a function of time constant C1R1. R1 is made variable to provide amplitude control. By using a small portion of the charging curve a linear scan may be obtained.

**Fig. 8.1** Sawtooth generation:
(a) simple transistor circuit,
(b) waveforms

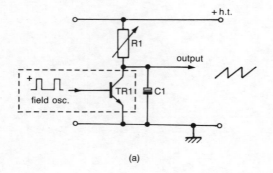

(a)

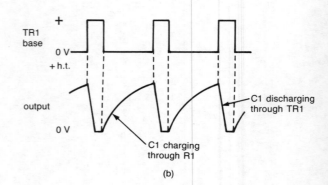

(b)

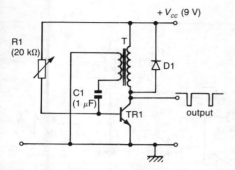

**Fig. 8.2** Blocking oscillator

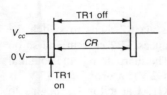

**Fig. 8.3** Output of a blocking oscillator

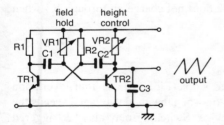

**Fig. 8.4** Astable multivibrator

## Blocking oscillator

A typical blocking oscillator circuit is shown in Fig. 8.2. The action of the circuit hinges around the fact that due to transformer coupling, a voltage is induced into the base only when the collector current is varying up or down. In one case the feedback is positive and in the other it is negative. When the circuit is first switched on, the transistor conducts and the collector current increases, thereby producing a feedback voltage at the base in such a way as to switch the transistor further on. When saturation is reached, the collector current ceases to increase and an opposite voltage is induced at the base which this time turns the transistor off. The transistor is held in the off state by the negative charge on capacitor C1 until the latter is sufficiently discharged through resistor R1 when the transistor switches on again and so on.

The output from a blocking oscillator is a narrow pulse waveform (Fig. 8.3). The width or mark of the pulse is determined by the parameters of the transformer while the space is determined by time constant C1R1. It follows that the frequency of the oscillator may be varied by changing the value of R1.

Depending on the parameters of the transformer, a large overshoot in the collector voltage may be obtained as the transistor switches off. This overshoot voltage may be of such a magnitude as to exceed the maximum rateable collector voltage resulting in damage to the transistor. In order to protect the transistor, a diode D1 is connected across the primary winding of the transformer. The diode, which is normally reverse biased, will conduct only when the collector voltage exceeds the d.c. supply $V_{cc}$.

## Multivibrator

The astable multivibrator (Fig. 8.4) may also be used to produce a field timebase waveform. The multivibrator uses two separate time constants, C1VR1 for the mark and C2R2 for the space. The pulse waveform at the collector of TR2 is converted into a sawtooth by capacitor C3.

Time constant C1VR1 determines the period that TR2 remains off during which time C3 charges up to provide the scan part of the sawtooth. The setting of VR1 thus controls the frequency of the output. The amplitude on the other hand may be varied by VR2 to control the picture height. Time constant C2R2 determines the duration for which C3 remains discharged, i.e the flyback.

A simpler astable multivibrator that is successfully used in TV receivers is the emitter coupled type shown in Fig. 8.5 in which C1 forms part of both time constants. The negative-going sync. pulse switches TR1 off and TR2 on. C1 with its left-hand plate at $+15$ V begins to charge up very quickly through TR2 forcing its right-hand plate (TR2 base) towards zero. As TR2 base approaches zero, current through TR2 begins to decrease and its collector voltage begins to

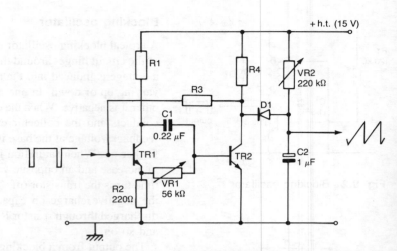

**Fig. 8.5** Astable multivibrator

increase which when fed to TR1 base via R3 tends to switch the transistor off which in turn further reduces TR2 current and so on until TR1 saturates and TR2 turns off. The sharp drop in the potential of TR1 collector (from 15 V to about 2 V), a drop of −13 V, is transferred to the base of TR2 via C1. Capacitor C1 begins to discharge through VR1/R2 towards TR1 emitter voltage of +2 V. As it crosses the zero line, TR2 switches on and so on. It is arranged that just before TR2 switches on 'naturally', the sync. pulse arrives to trigger the multivibrator at precisely the right time. In other words, the natural frequency of the oscillator is adjusted by VR1 to be slightly lower that the field frequency so that the arrival of the sync. pulse ensures field lock.

C2/VR2 is a ramp generator network which provides the sawtooth waveform with VR2 controlling its amplitude, i.e. the picture height. D1 is an isolating diode conducting only when TR2 saturates. This is necessary to ensure that C2 does not charge up through R4 when TR2 is turned off.

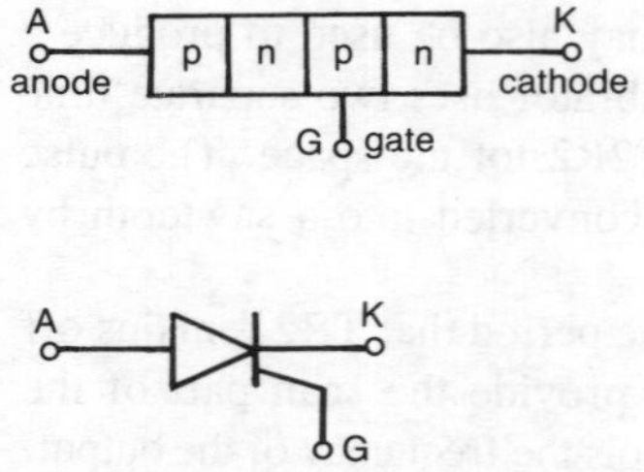

## Thyristor oscillator

The silicon controlled rectifier, s.c.r. (Fig. 8.6), is a four-layer pnpn switching device which turns on when the anode voltage exceeds the breakdown voltage of the device. Switching may also be triggered by the application of a positive pulse to the gate. When the s.c.r. is conducting, the voltage across it falls to a small value known as the **holding voltage**. Once the s.c.r. is switched on, it will only turn off when the anode potential falls below the holding voltage.

A more versatile switching device is the silicon controlled switch, s.c.s., shown in Fig. 8.7. In this case a second gate G2 known as the **anode gate** is brought out as a control terminal. This additional gate may also be used to trigger the device on. This time, however, a negative pulse is necessary. Both the s.c.r. and the s.c.s. are commonly known as thyristors.

**Fig. 8.6** The silicon controlled rectifier (s.c.r.) and its symbol

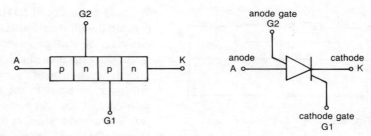

**Fig. 8.7** The silicon controlled switch (s.c.s.) and its symbol

A self-oscillating thyristor using a s.c.s. is shown in Fig. 8.8. When the supply voltage, h.t., is switched on, capacitor C1 charges up through R1 at a rate determined by time constant C1R1. When the voltage across C1 exceeds the breakdown voltage of the thyristor, the latter turns on and discharges the capacitor very quickly through R2. The thyristor remains switched on until its anode potential falls below its holding potential, i.e. when the capacitor is almost fully discharged. When that happens, the thyristor switches off and the capacitor begins to charge up again and so on. A sawtooth waveform is obtained across C1 while a pulse output is obtained across R2. Synchronisation is obtained by feeding the field sync. pulses into one of the control gates, a positive-going pulse to the cathode gate or a negative-going pulse to the anode gate. The natural frequency of the oscillator is determined by time constant C1R1.

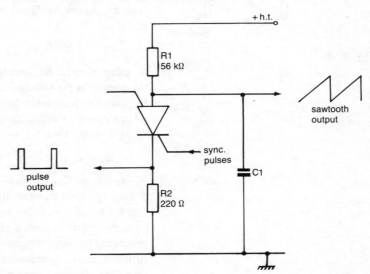

**Fig. 8.8** Self-oscillating thyristor

### Field scanning waveform

A linear deflection is obtained when a sawtooth current waveform is fed into the scan coils. However, because of the inductance presented by the scan coils, the voltage necessary to obtain a linear current through the coils may not be of a linear shape depending on the ratio of the resistance of the coil to its inductance, $r/XL$. At the

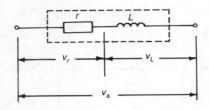

**Fig. 8.9**

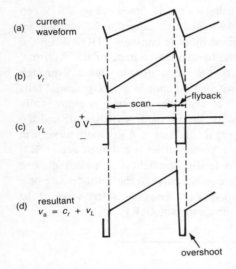

**Fig. 8.10**

low field frequency of 50 Hz the reactance of the field coils is small compared with their resistance making the coils mainly resistive. In this case the voltage waveform is almost the same as the current.

Consider the inductor shown in Fig. 8.9 in which $r$ represents the effective resistance of the inductor and $L$ its inductance. The applied voltage $v_a$ is equal to the vectorial sum of the voltage across the resistance, $v_r$ and that across the inductance $v_L$. If the applied voltage was a sine wave, then all the other waveforms would be sinusoidal as well. The relationship between these waveforms could then be represented by a simple vector diagram to show their relative amplitude and phase. For an applied waveform other than a sine wave, i.e. a waveform that contains one or more harmonics, each harmonic suffers a different amount of attenuation and phase shift. Current and voltage waveforms will therefore differ not only in their amplitude and phase but in their shape as well. It is not possible in these cases to draw one simple phasor diagram since each phasor represents a sine wave at one particular frequency. A large number of phasor diagrams is therefore necessary, one for each harmonic.

A simple way of deducing the required shape of the applied voltage is to add the waveform across the resistance to that across the inductance, $v_r + v_L$ as shown in Fig. 8.10. In (a) the sawtooth current waveform which is necessary for a linear scan is shown. As far as resistance $r$ is concerned, the voltage across it, $v_r$, is in phase with the current as shown in (b). For inductance $L$, the voltage across it

$$v_L = L \, \mathrm{d}i/\mathrm{d}t$$

In other words, the greater the rate of change of current, $\mathrm{d}i/\mathrm{d}t$, the greater is the voltage across the inductance. For the scan part of the current waveform the rate of change of current, $\mathrm{d}i/\mathrm{d}t = c$, where $c$ is a constant determined by the slope of the scan. Since $v_L = L \, \mathrm{d}i/\mathrm{d}t$, then for the scan part only

$$v_L = L \times c = k$$

where $k$ is another constant. It follows therefore that in order to obtain a linearly rising current, the voltage applied across a pure inductor $L$ must be of a constant value or d.c. (Fig. 8.10(c)).

At the end of the scan the current reverses and $\mathrm{d}i/\mathrm{d}t$ sharply increases producing the large negative-going edge shown in (c). For the duration of the flyback, $v_L$ remains constant but this time at a higher value than that obtained during the scan since the rate of change of the current is larger during the flyback than during the scan. At the end of the flyback, the current reverses again to produce the positive-going edge shown in (c) and so on.

If the two waveforms $v_r$ and $v_L$ are now added, we get the resultant or total waveform $v_a$ shown in (d). While the inductance has an insignificant effect on the scan part of the waveform, it is responsible for the overshoot produced during the flyback.

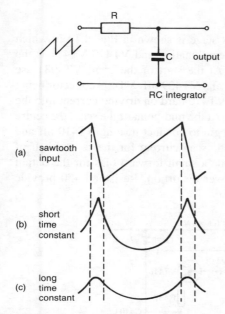

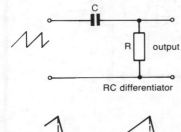

**Fig. 8.11** The effect of an integrator on a sawtooth waveform

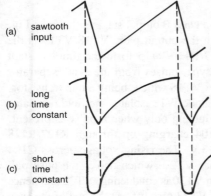

**Fig. 8.12** The effect of a differentiator on a sawtooth waveform

**Fig. 8.13** Tilted parabola

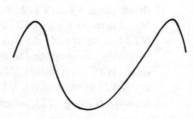

## Linearity or shaping networks

The field scan waveform requires further modification to ensure a linear display on the tube face. Waveform correction (or distortion) is necessary where transformer coupling is used between the output stage and the scan coils. In this case the sawtooth waveform has to be corrected to overcome the distorting effect of the magnetising current taken by the transformer. Correction is also required because of the flat surface of the tube face. This correction, known as the S-correction, is more noticeable on the line scan and will be discussed in detail in the next chapter. It is normal to include an effective shaping or correction network involving a combination of differentiators and integrators with more than one linearity control as part of the field timebase.

Consider an integrator fed with a sawtooth waveform (Fig. 8.11). The sawtooth consists of a fundamental and a number of harmonics. The integrator which is a low-pass filter attenuates the high-frequency harmonics slowing down the rate of change of the waveform and rounding the edges. The result is the parabola shown in (b). An integrator with a longer time constant (i.e. a filter with a lower cut-off frequency) would remove more high-frequency harmonics resulting in the parabola shown in (c).

The effect of a differentiator on a sawtooth waveform is shown in Fig. 8.12. The differentiator being a high-pass filter will attenuate the low frequency components resulting in sharper corners and faster rising edges as shown in (b). A differentiator with a shorter time constant (i.e. a filter with a higher cut-off frequency) would produce the sharper waveform shown in (c).

It is possible therefore to distort the sawtooth in such a way as to increase or decrease the scanning rate for all or part of the scan. Further changes in the shape of the scan may be produced by adding a sawtooth waveform to a parabola to obtain a tilted parabola (Fig. 8.13). This addition is normally carried out by current or voltage feedback. Current feedback involves the monitoring of the scan waveform using a small resistor $(1-5\,\Omega)$ connected in series with the field scan coils. The voltage which is developed across the resistor is fed back to the input of the field drive amplifier via a correction network.

## Class B field output

A typical class B field output stage is shown in Fig. 8.14 in which
VT408/VT409 is the driver combination and VT410/VT411 is the
complementary output pair. At the start of the scan, VT408 base
voltage is low turning VT408 and VT409 off. VT409 collector being
at almost h.t. potential turns VT410 hard on driving current into the
field scan coils. VT411 is off. At the mid-point of the scan, the centre
of the picture, VT408/409 begin to conduct turning VT410 off and
VT411 on, which provides the scan current for the second half of
the picture. W411/412 provide a small forward bias for the output
transistors to prevent cross-over distortion. Resistor R450 provide
d.c. feedback for bias stability.

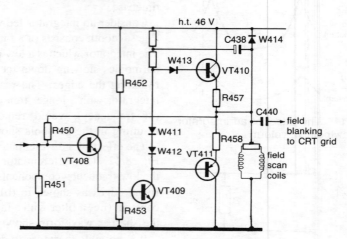

**Fig. 8.14** Class B field output stage
(Ferguson 8000 colour chassis)

## Practical field timebase

A practical field timebase with a class B output stage is shown in Fig.
8.15 in which VT23/VT24 are the output pair, VT18/VT19 is the
field oscillator and C102/R117/R116/R115 form the time constant
network. Positive-going field sync. pulses from the sync. separator
are fed via W18 into the base of VT18 which, being a pnp transistor,
turns off to start the flyback. Diode W18 isolates the field oscillator
from the sync. separator, conducting only when a pulse is present.
The ramp is produced by C104 charging up through R127/R128
towards the h.t. supply of 11.3 V. The rising voltage across C104
turns on the high-gain amplifier VT20, which drives the push-pull
driver stage VT21/VT22. When VT20 is conducting, VT22 and hence
VT24 turn on while VT21 and VT23 turn off. At the end of the scan
VT24 is saturated. At this point, a positive-going pulse from the
multivibrator is applied to the bases of VT21 and VT22, via isolating
diode W19. Transistors VT22 and VT24 are turned off, while VT21
and VT23 are turned on, VT23 collector potential rises to d.c. supply,
forward biasing W21 which short circuits C109. The rapid change

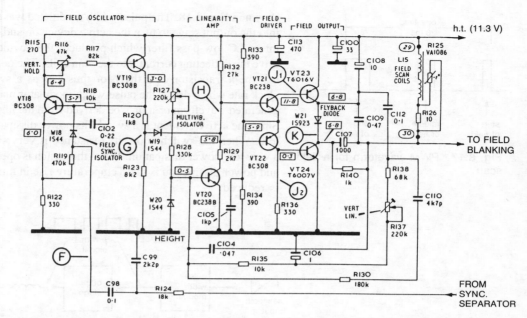

**Fig. 8.15** Complete field timebase (Ferguson 1690 mono chassis)

in the current through the scan coils produces a back e.m.f. making VT24 collector rise at a rate determined by the *L/r* ratio of the scan coils. When VT24 collector potential exceeds the supply voltage, diode W21 turns off. Capacitor C109 is then placed across the scan coils which starts to oscillate or ring. The flyback rises sharply to the first positive peak voltage of the ringing sine wave and decreases attempting to go to the negative peak voltage. Well before it reaches negative peak, W21 conducts which terminates the ringing as the energy stored in the scan coils is fed into the supply rails via W21 and VT23. This continues until the scan begins again and so on. Linearity correction is obtained by a feedback network containing linearity amplifier VT20. The field sawtooth waveform is modified with a parabola produced by integrator R138/R137/C106. Further shape correction is obtained by differentiator C110/R130.

## Switched mode (class D) field output

The basic principle of the switched mode (also known as class D) output stage is shown in Fig. 8.16 in which a pulse train is fed into an RC low-pass filter. As can be seen, the pulses are smoothed with the capacitor charging up to the mean value of the input pulse. Since the mean value is determined by the mark-to-space ratio of the input pulse, then a varying mark-to-space ratio, i.e. a pulse-width modulated waveform, produces a varying charge across the capacitor. A linearly increasing capacitor voltage, a timebase ramp scan, may thus be produced if the mark-to-space ratio of the input pulse is gradually increased as shown in Fig. 8.17.

A simplified block diagram for a switched-mode output stage is

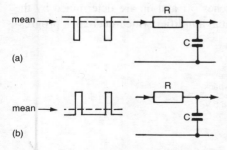

**Fig. 8.16** Mean (d.c.) level of a pulse-width modulated waveform: (a) high mark-to-space ratio (b) low mark-to-space ratio

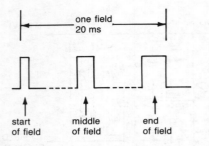

**Fig. 8.17** PWM waveform for a field scan

shown in Fig. 8.18. The pulse-width modulated waveform is first fed into the output stage to turn the active device on and off before going into a LC low-pass filter which produces the sawtooth waveform to drive the deflecting current into the scan coils. The ouput device which may be a transistor or a thyristor thus acts as a switch. The pulse clock rate which drives the pulse-width modulator may be a separately generated waveform or it may be derived from the line scanning pulse. Since the active element is a switch, its power dissipation is extremely low. When the switch is on, its resistance is very small resulting in a very low power dissipation. When the switch is open, current ceases and power dissipation is nil. Temperature rise in minimised and cost is reduced.

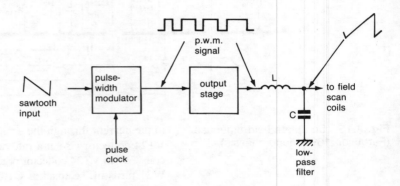

**Fig. 8.18** Switched-mode (class D) field output stage

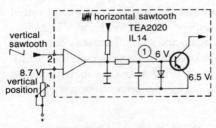

**Fig. 8.19** Pulse-width modulator (TEA 2029 part)

A pulse-width modulator circuit used by sync. processing chip TEA 2029 is shown in Fig. 8.19. The differential amplifier has two inputs, a field sawtooth at pin 2 and a field shift correcting voltage on pin 1. The field sawtooth from the differential amplifier together with a line sawtooth are applied to the modulator transistor TR1. The modulator transistor operates as a comparator with a threshold voltage of 6.5 V, that being the voltage at its emitter. TR1 will switch off only when the its base voltage falls below 6.5 V, at which point the collector voltage rises to supply (Fig. 8.20). The points on the line sawtooth at which TR1 switches off and on are determined by the ouput voltage of the differential amplifier which decreases progres-

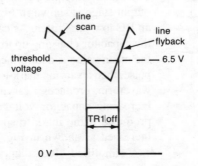

**Fig. 8.20**

sively as the scan proceeds from start to finish. This causes the line
sawtooth waveform to shift progressively deeper into the switching
switching threshold of TR1 as shown in Fig. 8.21 resulting in a linearly
changing mark-to-space ratio.

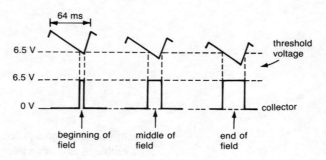

**Fig. 8.21**

# 9 Line timebase

Like most small signal processes, line synchronisation and generation are availble as part of an integrated circuit. Where discrete components are employed, two types of oscillators are normally used in the line timebase, the Hartley and the blocking oscillators. While the blocking oscillator is more efficient, the Hartley is more popular because of its good frequency stability which means that a smaller pull-in range may be used by the flywheel discriminator, thus improving its noise immunity.

A line timebase circuit using a blocking oscillator (VT15) is shown in Fig. 9.1 in which diodes W6 and W7 form the flywheel discriminator with C78/R82/C79/R85/C62 as the smoothing low-pass filter. Feedback transformer L12 is tuned by C83. It should be noted that a reactance stage is not necessary which is one of the advantages of the blocking oscillator over the Hartley. VT15 is switched on when C84 discharges through R84/R83 raising the base voltage to a level

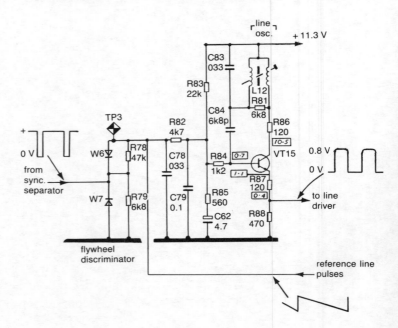

**Fig. 9.1** Line timebase circuit (Ferguson 1690 mono chassis)

sufficient to forward bias the transistor. By varying the d.c. control voltage from the flywheel discriminator to VT15 base, the time at which the switching occurs is also varied, thus changing the frequency of operation.

### The Hartley oscillator

The Hartley oscillator is a sine wave oscillator with a tuned circuit as the collector load. Feedback is achieved by tapping the inductor and feeding part of the output back to the base. By using a large reverse bias it is possible to make the transistor turn off for part of the cycle and saturate for the other part. In this way the transistor is made to act as a switch. A line oscillator circuit employing a Hartley is shown in Fig. 9.2. The tapping in inductor L1 is decoupled to chassis via C1. The signal across the lower part of tuned circuit L1/C1 is fed back to the base of TR1 via C2. A large amount of positive feedback is employed with C2 providing class C self biasing for TR1. The level of this reverse bias is determined by time constant C2R1. The tuned circuit oscillates so long as energy in the form of collector current is fed into it at regular intervals. The transistor being biased beyond cut off will conduct only for the positive peaks of the sine wave fedback into its base. The waveform at the base will have its positive peaks clipped as the b—e junction becomes forward biased as shown in Fig. 9.3(a). The pulsating current through the transistor, as the latter switches on and off, produces the square wave shown in (b) across emitter resistor R3.

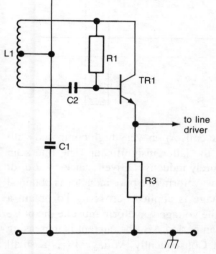

**Fig. 9.2**  Hartley line oscillator

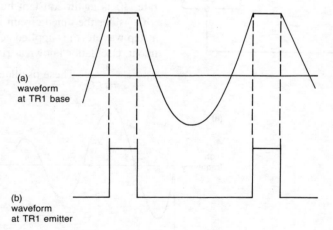

(a) waveform at TR1 base

(b) waveform at TR1 emitter

**Fig. 9.3**  Waveforms for circuit in Fig. 9.2

### The line scan waveform

The purpose of the line timebase is to provide the appropriate deflection current through the line scan coils. The current waveform required to produce linear deflection is, as in the case of the field scan, a sawtooth waveform. However, at the relatively high line

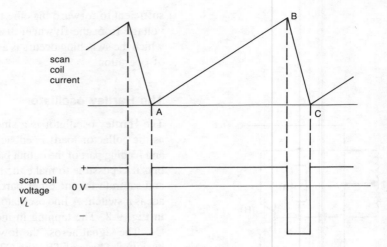

scan coil current

scan coil voltage $V_L$

0 V

**Fig. 9.4** Line scan coil current and voltage waveforms

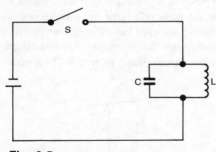

S

C

L

**Fig. 9.5**

frequency the reactance of the coil, $X_L$, is very high compared with its d.c. resistance, rendering the latter insignificant. The line scan coils may then be treated as purely inductive. Given that $V_L = L\,\mathrm{d}i/\mathrm{d}t$ it follows that a linear current waveform in a pure inductor is obtained when a constant or d.c. voltage is applied across it. To obtain a sawtooth current waveform, the voltage waveform must be the pulse shown in Fig. 9.4. For the scan period AB, the current is increasing at a small and constant rate. Consequently, voltage $V_L$ is a small positive value which remains constant for that duration. For the flyback period, BC, the current is decreasing at a high and constant rate. $V_L$ is again constant but this time large and negative.

Consider the tuned circuit in Fig. 9.5. When the switch is closed, a step waveform is applied across the tuned circuit and energy is fed into it. Oscillation known as ringing takes place at a resonant frequency $f_0 = \dfrac{1}{2\pi\sqrt{LC}}$ . These oscillations take place because electromagnetic

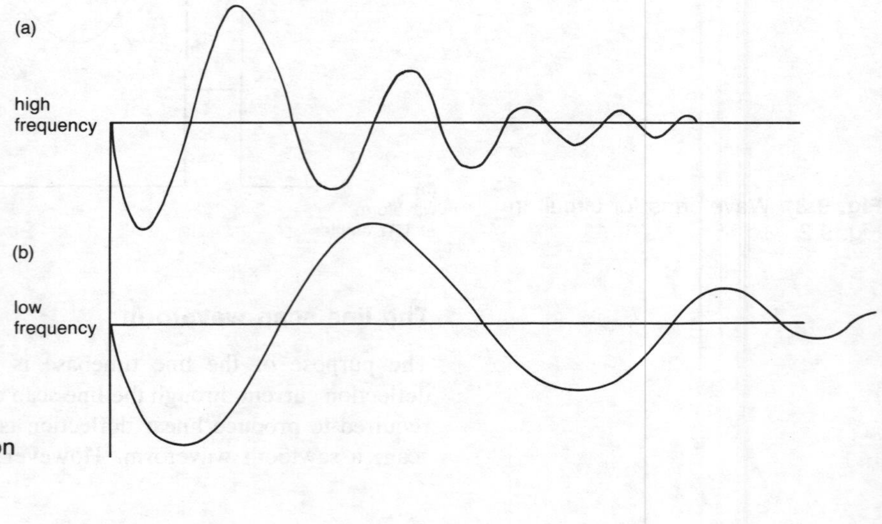

(a)

high frequency

(b)

low frequency

**Fig. 9.6** Damped oscillation

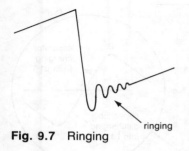

**Fig. 9.7** Ringing

energy in the scan coils is continuously transformed into electrostatic energy in the capacitor and vice versa. Current therefore flows from the coil to the capacitor and back again. Ideally, this ringing should continue indefinitely since there is no power or energy loss in either a pure inductor or a pure capacitor. However, due to losses caused mainly by the very small resistance of inductor, ringing gradually dies out producing what is known as damped oscillation (Fig. 9.6).

Similar oscillation or ringing occurs when a sharp change in voltage is applied across an inductor. The tuning frequency in this case is the self-capacitance of the coil as well as any stray capacitance due to other components. In the case of the line scan, ringing occurs at the beginning of each flyback as shown in Fig. 9.7 with a consequent distortion on the left-hand side of the picture on the tube face.

It is possible to remove the effect of ringing by shunting the scan coils with a damping resistor. This, however, will result in a large waste of energy reducing the power available for beam deflection and reducing the angle of deflection of the tube.

### Efficiency diode

To avoid ringing without the loss of power, an efficiency diode is used. This technique is based on the utilisation of the energy stored in the scan coils due to the flyback to provide the first half of the scan. It involves a switching network which directs the transfer of energy to and from the scan coils to obtain the required waveform.

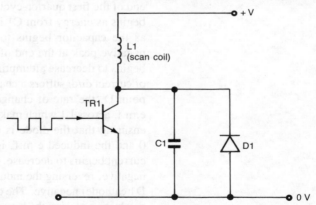

**Fig. 9.8** Use of efficiency diode, D1

Such a circuit using a parallel transistor−diode switch is shown in Fig. 9.8 in which L1 is the scan coil, D1 is the efficiency diode and TR1 is the line output transistor. When TR1 is switched on by a positive edge to its base at time $t_1$ (Fig. 9.9), a constant h.t. voltage is applied across scan coil L1. A linearly increasing current is therefore obtained forming part AB of the scan. The current continues to rise until point B when at time $t_2$ a negative step to the base switches TR1 off. At this point TR1 collector suffers a sudden jump from almost chassis potential to + h.t. This positive voltage ensures that D1

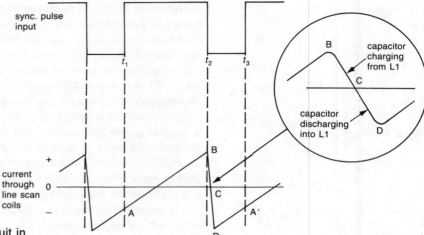

sync. pulse
input

current
through
line scan
coils

**Fig. 9.9** Waveforms for circuit in
Fig. 9.8

remains non-conducting. C1 is now effectively connected across L1.
The large change in current in L1 produces ringing at a frequency
determined by C1 and other stray capacitors. Energy due to the sudden
change of current through L1 is transferred to C1 to commence ringing
oscillation at point B. When C1 is fully charged, point C on the
flyback, charging current drops to zero as the ringing comes to the
end of the first quarter-cycle of oscillation. The second quarter-cycle
begins as energy from C1 is transferred to L1. The current reverses
as the capacitor begins to discharge. When the cycle reaches its
negative peak at the end of the first half-cycle, point D, the current
begins to decrease attempting to go to zero again. The rate of change
of current $di/dt$ suffers a change of direction. Before the negative peak,
point D, the rate of change of current is positive. This induces an
e.m.f. across L1 which makes TR1 collector (and D1 cathode) positive
ensuring that the diode is off. At the negative peak itself, $di/dt =
0$ and the induced e.m.f. is also zero. After the negative peak, the
current begins to decrease. The rate of change of current is therefore
negative, reversing the induced e.m.f. and making TR1 collector (and
D1 cathode) negative. The diode conducts. Its effect is similar to TR1
conducting placing the h.t. across L1 to start the scan. Current through
L1 rises linearly to form about 30% of the scan up to A′ when TR1
is switched on at time $t_3$ by a positive edge to the base and so on.

## S-correction

In order to compensate for the flat surface of the tube face, correction
of the line scan waveform is necessary. This correction, known as
symmetrical or S-correction, becomes increasingly important with
wide-angle deflection tubes.

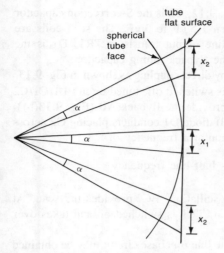

**Fig. 9.10**  Effect of flat tube screen

As can be seen from Fig. 9.10 an equal angular deflection of the beam scans a smaller distance at the centre compared with the distance it scans at the two ends of the line. Thus to obtain a linear picture scan using a flat tube face, a non-linear angular deflection is necessary. The purpose of the non-linearity is to slow the rate of change of the angular deflection at both ends of the scan as shown in Fig. 9.11. Since the current through the line scan coils is responsible for the angular deflection, the corrected waveform must be of the same shape.

The scan part of the waveform in Fig. 9.11(a) approximates a half-cycle of the sine wave shown in (b) and may be simply obtained by connecting a capacitor in series with the scan coils. The value of the capacitor is chosen so that it resonates with the scan coils at a frequency slightly higher than half of the line frequency, 7.8 kHz approximately. This provides a time duration from A to B of

$$\frac{1}{2} \text{ period} = \frac{1}{2} \times \frac{1}{7.8} = 64 \ \mu s \text{ (approx.)}$$

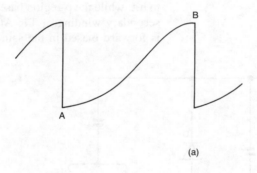

(a)

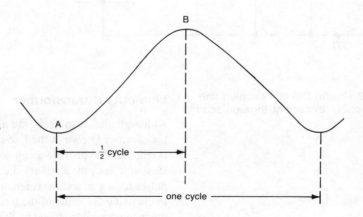

(b)

**Fig. 9.11**  (a) S-correction waveform, (b) Half-line frequency sine wave

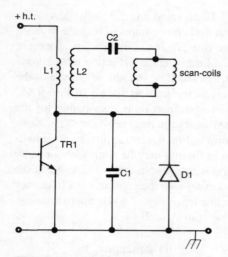

**Fig. 9.12** Line output stage with S-correction capacitor C2

In the line output stage in Fig. 9.12, C2 is the S-correction capacitor which has a value of between 1.5 µF to 3 µF. The scan coils are transformer-coupled to the line output transistor TR1. D1 is the efficiency diode and C1 is the flyback tuning capacitor.

Modern TV receivers employ direct coupling as shown in Fig. 9.13. At the end of the scan, TR1 is switched off, tuned circuit L1/C1/C2 is pulsed into oscillation to provide the flyback AB (Fig. 9.13(b)). At the negative peak (point B) diode D1 conducts placing C2 across L1 to commence an oscillation at a frequency of

$$\frac{1}{2\pi\sqrt{LC}} = \text{half-line frequency.}$$

The first half-cycle of this oscillation, BC, provides the scan. At approximately 1/3 of the scan, TR1 is switched on and takes over from the diode and so on.

Further simplification of the line timebase circuit may be obtained by using the b–c junction of the output transistor TR1 as the efficiency diode as illustrated in Fig. 9.14. The polarity of the b–c junction is the same as the polarity of an efficiency diode had the latter been connected, namely that the n-region collector(cathode) is connected to h.t. while the p-region base (anode) is connected to chassis via the secondary winding of T1. At the end of the scan the b–c junction is forward biased in the same manner as an efficiency diode.

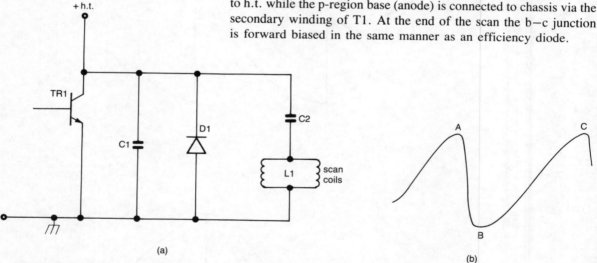

(a)

(b)

**Fig. 9.13** (a) Directly coupled line scan coils, (b) current through scan coils

## Line output transformer

Although the scan coils are not normally transformer-coupled, a transformer known as the line output transformer, LOPT (Fig. 9.14) is employed to provide a number of functions including the extra high tension, e.h.t., the auxiliary d.c. supplies, the boost voltage, the gating pulses for a.g.c. and the reference pulse for the flywheel discriminator. In choosing the value of the tuning capacitor for the line output stage, the inductance introduced by the line output transformer must be taken into account.

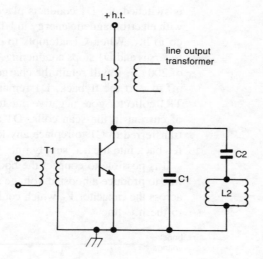

**Fig. 9.14** Line output using b-c junction as efficiency diode

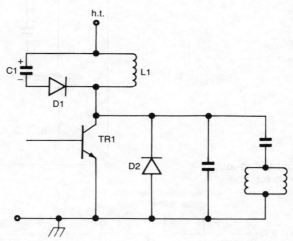

**Fig. 9.15** Line output with boost capacitor and diode D1, C1

## Boost voltage

One important function of the line output transformer is to provide the high d.c. supply voltage of between 30–90 V required by the video, line and field output amplifiers. For receivers operating from the mains supply, this d.c. voltage may be obtained by rectifying the mains voltage. However, this is not possible for battery operated receivers and a boost voltage from the LOPT is used.

The boost voltage is obtained by the use of an efficiency diode and a storage capacitor. Consider the circuit in Fig. 9.15 in which L1 is the primary winding of the line output transformer, D1 is the boost diode, C1 is the storage or boost capacitor and TR1 is the line output transistor. D1 is connected in such a way that it only allows charging current to flow through C1 and prevents the discharging current from flowing through L1 thus maintaining the charge across C1. When TR1 is switched on, D1 conducts placing C1 across L1. Ringing occurs with electromagnetic energy in L1 transferring to C1, which charges up to h.t. When C1 attempts to discharge through L1, the current reverses and D1 stops conducting. Provided C1 is large, in the region of 200 $\mu$F, it will retain the charge across it. When TR1 is switched off to start the flyback, D1 remains off. At the end of the flyback, TR1 collector goes negative due to the reversal of the rate of change of current in the scan coils. D1 and D2 conduct. Energy in L1 is transferred to C1 to replace any loss in its charge. Excess energy is fed back into the h.t. supply line. C1 thus remains charged up to h.t.

It is possible to connect the boost capacitor in series with the h.t. line to produce a boosted voltage as shown in Fig. 9.16. The charge across the capacitor $V_B$ which could exceed the h.t. potential is added to the h.t. line.

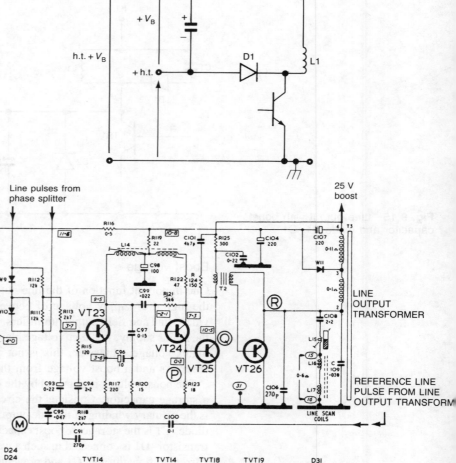

**Fig. 9.16** Line output with boost capacitor in series with h.t. line

**Fig. 9.17** Line timebase circuit (Ferguson 1590 mono chassis)

## Practical circuit

A line timbase circuit for a monochrome receiver using discrete components is shown in Fig. 9.17 in which W9/W10 is the flywheel discriminator, VT23 the reactance stage and VT24 is a Hartley oscillator. L14 and C99 form the oscillator tuned circuit. Self biasing is obtained by C99/R121. The output from the reactance stage, VT23, is effectively connected across the left-hand side of the winding of L14 and as such will determine the frequency of oscillation. W11 and C107 are the boost diode and capacitor respectively. The 25 V boost voltage is obtained from an h.t. line of only 11.6 V. VT26 is the line output transistor, C108 is the S-correction capacitor, C109 is the tuning capacitor and L15 is the line linearity control. Capacitor C106 is a flashover capacitor used to protect the output transistor from flashover inside the tube.

# 10 The sound channel

In the British television system, the sound information is frequency modulated on a separate carrier spaced 6 MHz away from the vision carrier. Following frequency changing at the tuner, the sound carrier is changed to an i.f. of 33.5 MHz and the vision carrier to an i.f. of 39.5 MHz. The difference between the two intermediate frequencies which remains at 6 MHz is known as the sound inter-carrier frequency and is used for demodulation purposes. In this way problems of sound distortion caused by the drift in the local oscillator at the tuner unit are overcome. This is because a drift in the oscillator frequencies causes the two i.f.s to change by the same amount, keeping the difference between them constant. Frequency drift does not have the same effect on the vision carrier since the latter is amplitude modulated.

The inter-carrier 6 MHz beat frequency is obtained from a device such as a diode which when used at the non-linear part of its characteristics produces the sum and difference of two separate input frequencies. The resulting 6 MHz beat frequency retains the frequency modulated information which when demodulated reproduces the original sound signal. Ideally the sound inter-carrier should have a constant amplitude. However, some amplitude modulation will be present caused by the vision i.f. which is amplitude modulated. This interference will cause what is known as **vision buzz** on the audio output unless removed by a limiting circuit before demodulation.

A block diagram of a sound channel is shown in Fig. 10.1. The output of the video detector stage is fed into a 6 MHz filter or trap before going into a limiting stage containing one or more clipping (or limiting) amplifiers. After frequency demodulation, the sound signal is amplified by a driver before going into the a.f. output stage and subsequently to the loudspeaker.

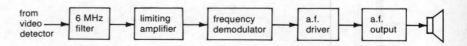

**Fig. 10.1**   Sound channel

## Frequency demodulators

In frequency modulation the carrier frequency deviates above and below its centre frequency in accordance with the amplitude of the modulating signal. The f.m. detector or demodulator thus has to convert the frequency deviations back into the original signal.

There are two main types of f.m. demodulators that are used in TV receivers: the ratio detector and the quadrature (coincidence) detector. The first uses discrete components and has the advantage of providing its own rejection of amplitude modulation. The second, though more complex, lends itself more easily for i.c. packaging and hence it is extensively used in modern TV receivers.

The operation of the f.m. detector is based on the fact that while the impedance of a tuned circuit is resistive at the resonant frequency, it becomes inductive if the frequency falls below the centre resonant frequency and capacitive if the frequency rises above the resonant frequency. Consider the LC circuit in Fig. 10.2(a). At the tuned frequency $f_0$, the circuit is purely resistive with voltage $v_0$ in phase with the current $i$ as shown in the phasor diagram in (b). However, if the frequency falls below the resonant frequency, voltage $v_0$ leads the current, and conversely if it rises above it, the voltage lags the current. The amount of phase shift is determined by the deviation away from the tuned frequency of the circuit. If the input to the circuit was at the sound inter-carrier then, provided the circuit is tuned to 6 MHz, the phase shift represents the original modulating sound signal. In the f.m. detector, this phase shift is translated into a voltage variation to reproduce the audio signal.

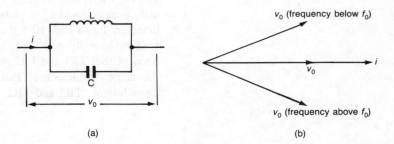

**Fig. 10.2** (a) Tuned circuit, (b) phasor diagram

(a)

(b)

## The quadrature (coincidence) detector

A schematic diagram of a quadrature frequency detector is shown in Fig. 10.3 in which L1C1 is tuned to 6 MHz. The input to the detector is a clipped sine wave from the preceding limiting stage. The two leads carrying the input signal connected directly to TR1 and TR3 are also applied across the tuned circuit via two capacitors C2 and C3. With respect to chassis, the two leads carry two clipped sine waves in anti-phase. At the centre frequency, L1C1 is purely resistive with its current $i$ in phase with the voltage across it, $v_0$. However, the

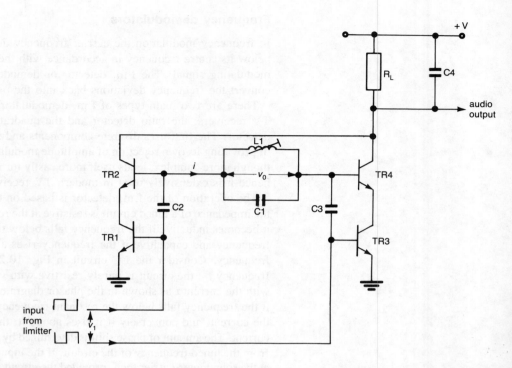

**Fig. 10.3** Quadrature (coincidence) detector

input voltage $v_1$ is applied across a circuit consisting of L1C1 in series with C2 and C3 as shown in Fig. 10.4(a). Since the reactance of C2 and C3 is large compared with the resistance of the tuned circuit, the current $i$ leads the input voltage $v_1$ by almost 90° (Fig. 10.4(b)). Thus at the centre frequency, $v_1$ and $v_0$ have a phase difference of 90°, usually known as 'phase quadrature', hence the name of the detector. From Fig. 10.3 it can be seen that current may flow into load resistor $R_L$ provided one of the following two coincidences occur: either TR1 and TR2 or TR3 and TR4 are switched on. Hence the name 'coincidence' that is sometimes used for this type of demodulator. TR1 and TR2 conduct on alternate half-cycles of the

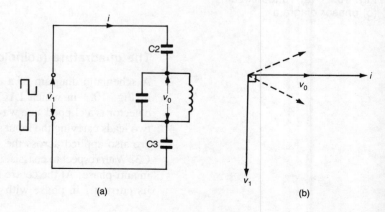

**Fig. 10.4**

(a)                                    (b)

input, $v_1$. TR2 and TR4 on the other hand conduct on alternate half-cycles of the voltage $v_0$ which is applied to the two transistors. However, since voltage $v_0$ is 90° out of phase with $v_1$, then the area of coincidence for TR1/TR2 and TR3/TR4 occurs for one quarter of a cycle only (90°) as shown in Fig. 10.5. As the input frequency

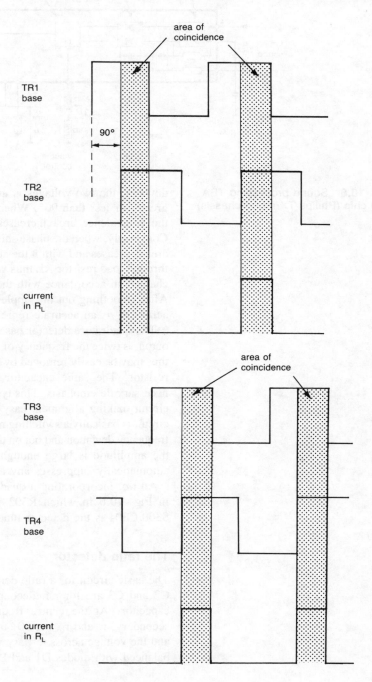

**Fig. 10.5** Waveforms for coincidence detector in Fig. 10.3

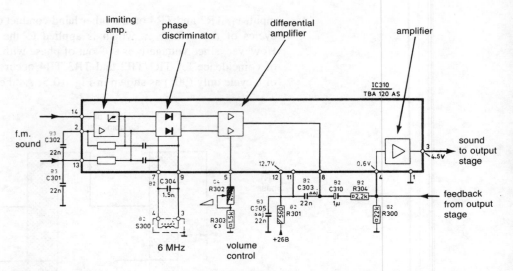

**Fig. 10.6** Sound processing TBA 120 chip (Philips TX mono chassis)

deviates, the two voltages $v_1$ and $v_0$ are no longer at 90° but either greater or less than 90°. When the phase shift is greater than 90°, the coincidence area increases and more current flows into RL. Conversely, when the phase shift is smaller than 90°, the coincidence area decreases and with it the current through RL. The mean current through load resistor RL thus varies with the phase shift which itself changes in accordance with the deviation of the f.m. inter-carrier. After smoothing out the ripple by capacitor C4, the output voltage across $R_L$ is an accurate representation of the modulating signal.

The quadrature detector has several advantages. The ripple at the output is twice the frequency of the incoming 6 MHz inter-carrier and thus may be easily removed by a capacitor connected across the load resistor. The same capacitor, if correctly chosen, produces the necessary de-emphasis. This type of detector requires a single tuned circuit making alignment easy to carry out. And finally, since the circuit is basically a switching network, the output depends solely on frequency deviation and not on the amplitude of the input and provided the amplitude is large enough for proper switching, the detector automatically suppresses any a.m. interference.

An i.c. incorporating a quadrature detector, TBA 120, is shown in Fig. 10.6 in which R302 is the volume control and inductor S300/C304 is the detector tuned circuit.

## The ratio detector

The basic circuit for a ratio detector is shown in Fig. 10.7 in which C2 and C3 are for r.f. decoupling and C4 is an a.m. decoupling capacitor. At the centre frequency the voltages induced in the secondary, $v_a$ and $v_b$, are 90° out of phase with the primary voltage and the voltage across tertiary winding $v_t$. The circuit is completely balanced with diodes D1 and D2 conducting equally to give a zero

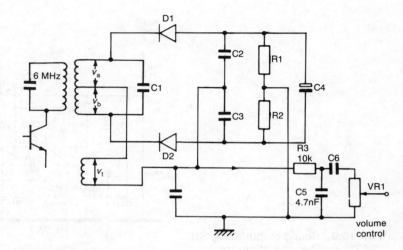

**Fig. 10.7**   Ratio detector circuit

output. As the frequency deviates away from 6 MHz, the phase difference is no longer 90° but either greater or less than 90° and the currents through the diodes are no longer equal. An output voltage is produced which is a measure of the deviation.

### De-emphasis

It is common for f.m. broadcasting to introduce pre-emphasis at the transmitter in which the high-frequency audio signals are boosted in comparison with middle and low frequencies. The purpose is to swamp most of the noise which also tends to be predominantly high-frequency. At the receiving end the signal must be subjected to de-emphasis by attenuating the treble or high frequency content in a similar but opposite way to the emphasis at the transmitter. Emphasis is carried out by the use of a filter and is expressed in terms of the time constant of the filter. In the UK a pre-emphasis of 50 $\mu$s is used. A de-emphasis filter with a time constant of 50 $\mu$s must therefore be used in the receiver to restore the audio frequencies to their proper relative levels. In Fig. 10.7, resistor R3/C5 is a filter circuit, with a time constant of 47 $\mu$s which provides the necessary de-emphasis.

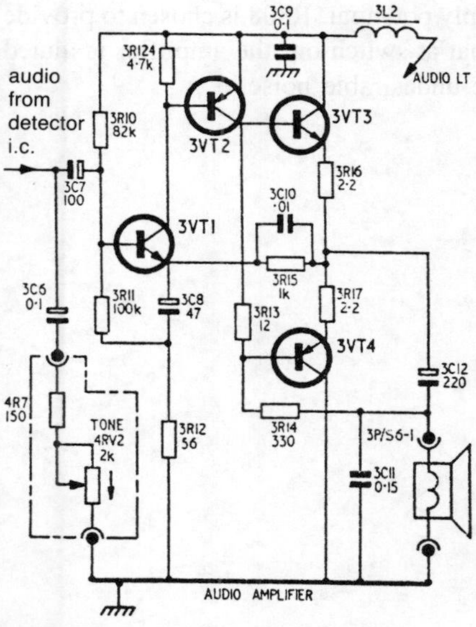

### A practical audio output stage

The circuit of an audio output amplifier used in a monochrome receiver is shown in Fig. 10.8 in which 3VT1 and 3VT2 form a d.c. coupled driver pair and 3VT3 and 3VT4 are the complementary output transistors. A number of feedback loops are used. The main one 3R15/3C10 provides d.c. and selective a.c. feedback. 3R12 provides only a.c. feedback to the emitter of 3VT1 with the d.c. feedback path blocked by 3C8.

An audio stage employing i.c. SN76033N is shown in Fig. 10.9. The integrated circuit consists of preamplifier, driver and class B

**Fig. 10.8**   Sound output stage (Bush)

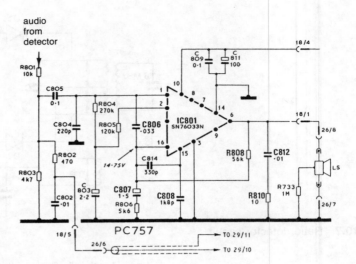

**Fig. 10.9** Sound output using SN 76033 amplifier chip (Ferguson)

complementary stages. The audio signal from the detector is applied to pin 1 via a tone control network R801/R802/R803/C802/C805/C804. Resistors R804 and R805 provide the d.c bias for the preamplifier with C803 as the decoupling capacitor. C812 and R810 are used to compensate for the reactive load of the loudspeaker. Integrated circuit amplifiers are capable of very high gains; consequently their frequency response must be 'tailored' to obtain the desired bandwidth and to prevent instability. R806/C807/C806 provide frequency tailoring while high frequency compensation is provided by C808. The i.c. does not operate until C807 has charged to approximately half the supply potential. R808 is chosen to provide a suitable time constant so that at switch on, the amplifier is muted for a short time to eliminate undesirable noise.

# 11 Colour burst processing

It will be recalled that the chrominance information is contained in a 4.43 MHz modulated subcarrier which forms part of the incoming composite video signal. Colour difference signals $B' - Y'$ and $R' - Y'$ are used to modulate the subcarrier which is then suppressed leaving two quadrature components, $U$ and $V$. At the receiver, the colour subcarrier is separated from the luminance signal and the two colour difference signals are then recovered by a synchronous demodulator using a phase-locked reference oscillator controlled by the colour burst. The luminance and colour difference signals are then applied to a matrix network, which performs the operation necessary to reproduce the original colour signals, $R'$, $G'$ and $B'$, that can be applied to a colour tube.

Colour decoding consists of four distinct parts: a colour burst processing section, a chrominance signal processing section, a matrix or mixer and a colour drive amplifier.

## Colour burst processing

The purpose of the colour burst processing section is to separate the burst signal from the chrominance information so that it may be used to recreate the subcarrier which has been suppressed at the transmitter. The subcarrier has to be restored in both its frequency and phase to ensure correct colour reproduction. Two subcarriers at 90° to each other have to be produced, one for each colour difference demodulator, $B' - Y'$ and $R' - Y'$. Furthermore, in the PAL system, the subcarrier for the $R' - Y'$ demodulator has to be phase-reversed on alternate lines. The burst processing section is also used to provide **automatic chrominance control** (a.c.c.) as well as the colour killer signal for monochrome-only transmission.

A block diagram for colour burst processing is shown in Fig. 11.1. The colour burst which consists of about 10 cycles of the original subcarrier is mounted on the back porch of the line sync. pulse. It is separated from the rest of the composite video by the burst gate amplifier. The burst gate amplifier is turned on by a delayed line

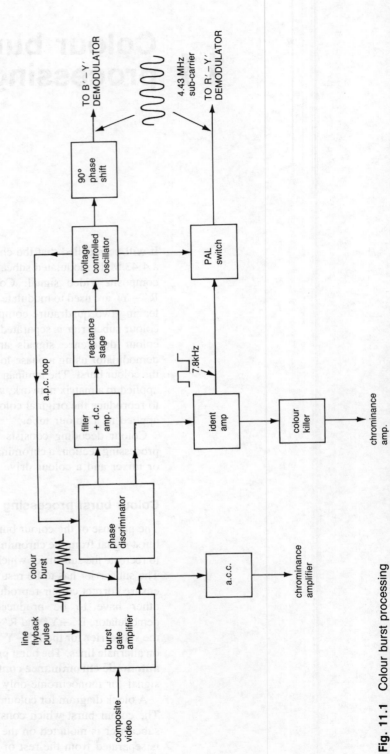

**Fig. 11.1** Colour burst processing

flyback pulse. The delay in the flyback pulse is necessary because the burst having been placed on the back porch does not coincide with the line sync. pulse, rather it arrives immediately after it. The delay ensures that the amplifier begins to conduct on the arrival of the burst. The burst gate amplifier allows the burst to go through a phase-locked loop network known as the **automatic phase control** (a.p.c.) consisting of the phase discriminator, filter, reactance stage and the voltage controlled oscillator. The phase discriminator compares the phase of the burst with the 4.43 MHz output of the voltage controlled crystal oscillator. If there is an error, a correction voltage is produced which after going through a low-pass filter is fed to a reactance stage to bring the frequency and phase of the oscillator into step with the burst. As was explained earlier, the burst signal is not of constant phase but swings $\pm 45°$ either side of the $-U$ phasor component to convey information of the phase reversal of the $V$ component at the transmitter. For this reason, the phase discriminator must compare the phase of the oscillator with the average phase of the burst signal. Averaging is accomplished by the introduction of a low-pass filter normally in the form of an a.c. negative feedback at the discriminator stage.

Referring to the block diagram in Fig. 11.1, the subcarrier for the $B' - Y'$ demodulator is obtained by the insertion of a simple 90° phase shift network at the output of the oscillator. The subcarrier for the $R' - Y'$ demodulator must suffer a phase reversal on alternate lines. To achieve this a square wave at half the line frequency is needed. A component of this frequency is present at the incoming signal because of the $\pm 45°$ phase change of the colour burst on alternate lines. Since one complete swing of the burst phase takes place every two lines, the frequency of the 'swing' is half the line frequency, i.e. $15\,625/2 = 7.8125$ kHz which is normally quoted as 7.8 kHz and referred to as the identification or '**Ident**' signal. After amplification, the Ident signal is fed into a PAL switch which reverses the phase of the 4.43 MHz oscillator signal on alternate lines.

Two other functions are derived from the burst processing section: colour killing and automatic chrominance control (a.c.c.) The purpose of the colour killer circuit is to close down the chrominance amplifier path on monochrome-only transmissions to prevent random colour noise appearing on the screen. The presence or otherwise of the colour burst indicates the type of transmission. The Ident signal is therefore used to provide a normal bias for the chrominance amplifier which will be turned off if the signal is absent.

Automatic chrominance control prevents varying propagation conditions from changing the amplitude of the chrominance signal in relation to the luminance. To realise this the gain of the chrominance amplifier is made variable by a control voltage in a similar way to the control of the gain of the i.f. stage by an a.g.c. signal. The a.c.c. control voltage must be proportional to the amplitude of the chrominance signal. This voltage cannot be derived from the actual

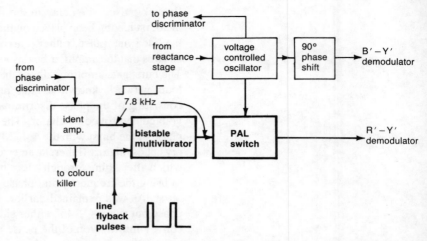

**Fig. 11.2** Use of a bistable to produce the Ident signal

chrominance signal during the active picture scan since this varies in amplitude as the colour information itself changes. It is derived instead by monitoring the amplitude of the colour burst. A fall in the amplitude of the burst signifies an attenuated chrominance. This is corrected by the a.c.c. control voltage going into the chrominance amplifier increasing its gain and vice versa.

An alternative method for producing the 7.8 kHz switching signal is to use a bistable multivibrator which is triggered once per line by pulses from the line timebase and synchronised by the Ident signal as shown in Fig. 11.2.

## Circuit using discrete components

The essential elements of a burst processing circuit using discrete components is shown in Fig. 11.3 in which VT109 is the burst gate amplifier, W106/W107 form the phase discriminator, VT110 is the

**Fig. 11.3** Colour burst processing using discrete components (Ferguson 8000 chassis)

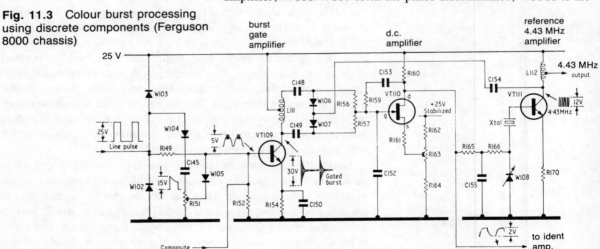

d.c. amplifier and VT111 is the crystal voltage controlled oscillator. Burst gate amplifier VT109 is switched on during the burst period by a positive-going delayed line flyback pulse. The line pulse is clamped by W102 to chassis and by W103 to the 25 V d.c. supply giving the pulse an amplitude of 25 V. After attenuation by R149 and R151, the line pulse appears at the base of burst gate amplifier, VT109, together with the composite chrominance signal including the colour burst. At the same time the 25 V line pulse forward biases diode W104 charging C145 via R151. The voltage across R151 rises and then decays as the capacitor begins to charge up. When the voltage across R151 falls to a value lower than the pulse voltage on VT109 base, diode W105 conducts and cuts off VT109. The time constant of C145/R151 is chosen such that VT109 is switched off at the conclusion of the burst. VT109 is held off during the active period of the line scan by the charge on capacitor C150 which holds the emitter positive with respect to the base until the next line pulse arrives. The amplified gated burst is then applied to the phase discriminator. Inductor L111 being centre-tapped will apply the burst in opposite phase across discriminator diodes W106 and W107. The burst is then compared with the signal from the reference oscillator applied to the centre of the diodes. Any difference in phase or frequency between the burst and the oscillator will result in a correction or error voltage across C152. The correction voltage is amplified by f.e.t. d.c. amplifier VT110 before going to the reactance stage, varicap diode W108, which controls the frequency and phase of the reference oscillator VT111. The averaging of the phase of the swinging burst is carried out by the filtering action of C153 and R159 together with the filtering and storage circuit R165/C155 which prevents sudden changes in oscillator frequency due to the intermittent nature of the burst. VT111 is a conventional crystal-controlled oscillator with the 4.43 MHz subcarrier being selected by self tuned inductor L112. Resistor R151 sets the timing of the burst gate and R163 provides the initial setting of the oscillator frequency/phase.

## The use of integrated circuits

In modern receivers, integrated circuits are extensively used for all major functions of the decoding channel. They invariably employ different circuit techniques to those used in discrete circuitry. In addition, a variety of functions are included in any one single i.c., such as subcarrier regeneration, demodulation and mixing. An early i.c. manufactured by Mullard, TBA 450, which performs the function of the automatic phase control of the subcarrier known as the reference combination i.c., is shown in Fig. 11.4. The reference oscillator has its frequency determined by a 4.43 MHz quartz crystal connected externally between pins 1 and 15. An output of the oscillator is compared with the gated burst signal by the burst phase detector. Any difference in phase/frequency results in an error voltage which is fed

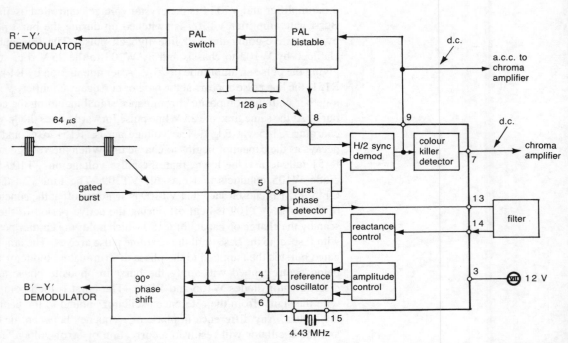

**Fig. 11.4** Reference combination TBA 450

back to the oscillator via a reactance stage and an externally connected filter. The amplitude of the output of the reference oscillator is stabilised by an amplitude control unit incorporated within the i.c. Two anti-phase subcarrier signals are available at pins 4 and 6 which are used to provide the quadrature subcarriers for the R′ − Y′ and B′ − Y′ demodulators as shown. The H/2 or half-line frequency synchronous demodulator compares the phase of the 7.8 kHz 'Ident' signal from the burst phase detector with the phase of the switching square wave produced by the bistable fed into pin 8. If the bistable

**Fig. 11.5** Colour burst processing employing TBA 395Q chip (Ferguson 9000 chassis)

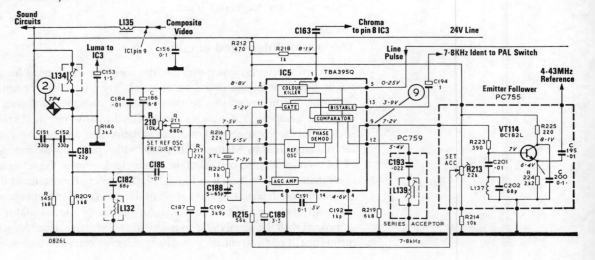

phase is incorrect the output voltage of the H/2 sync. demodulator (pin 9) rises to force the bistable to miss a step. When synchronism is obtained, the colour killer detector output at pin 7 rises and opens up the chrominance channel.

A circuit employing TBA 395 is shown in Fig. 11.5. The waveforms present at each pin are shown in Fig. 11.6. The composite video is fed via harmonic suppressor and 6 MHz filter L134/C151/C152 to the chrominance high-pass filter L132/C182/C181. The resulting chroma signal is coupled into pin 3 of the integrated circuit via C185. The a.c.c. (a.g.c.) amplifier maintains the chrominance signal at a constant level, predetermined by the setting of R213. After passing through the colour killer stage, it emerges at pin 1. C193 and L139 connected to pin 12 are tuned to 7.8 kHz to make the comparator sensitive at this frequency. The subcarrier output appears on pin 9 and is applied via emitter follower VT114 to the R′ − Y′ demodulator and via a phase shift to the B′ − Y′ demodulator.

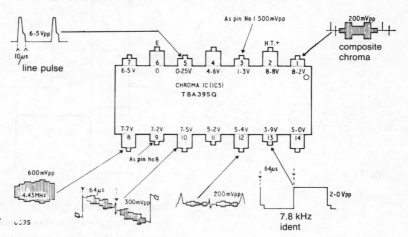

**Fig. 11.6**  Pin connections for TBA 395Q

### 8.86 MHz reference oscillator

The 90° phase-shift network used to provide the quadrature subcarrier waveform suffers from phase drift due to temperature change and ageing components. A more precise 90° phase may be provided by the use of a reference frequency twice the subcarrier, i.e. 8.86 MHz. This technique dispenses with the phase-shift network altogether as shown in Fig. 11.7. The 4.43 MHz subcarrier frequency is obtained by dividing the output of the reference oscillator by two. The output of the ÷2 network is then fed back to the phase discriminator to complete the automatic phase control (a.p.c.) loop. The divider provides two quadrature subcarriers which may then be fed directly to the B′ − Y′ demodulator and via a PAL switch to the R′ − Y′ demodulator.

The divider may consist of two bistables, one is made to trigger on the positive and the other on the negative half-cycles of the oscillator

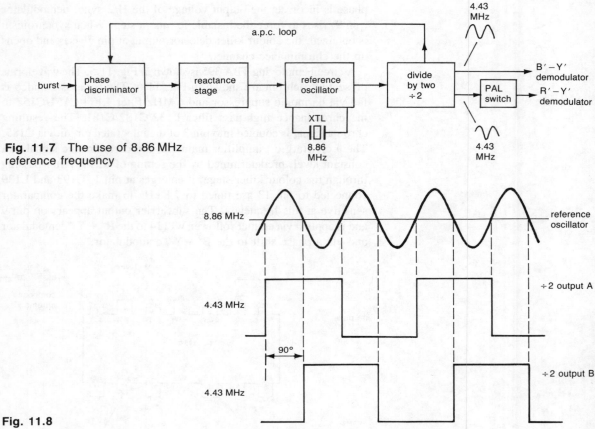

**Fig. 11.7** The use of 8.86 MHz reference frequency

**Fig. 11.8**

frequency as shown in Fig. 11.8. Each bistable divides the 8.86 MHz by two to provide a subcarrier of 4.43 MHz and at the same time provide a 90° phase difference between them.

## Passive subcarrier regeneration

It is possible to obtain the subcarrier directly from the burst, thus avoiding the use of a reference oscillator and its associated circuitry.

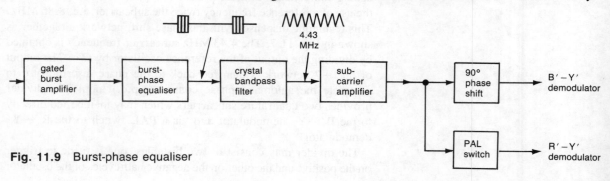

**Fig. 11.9** Burst-phase equaliser

If the burst is to be used directly, then it must have a constant phase. The PAL system, however, provides for a 'swinging' burst which suffers a 90° phase shift line by line. A burst-phase equaliser is therefore necessary as shown in Fig. 11.9. A subcarrier is then extracted by a very narrow, highly selective crystal bandpass filter. The output of the filter is a continuous 4.43 MHz sine wave which when amplified is ready to be used to provide the quadrature subcarriers to the two demodulators as shown.

# 12 Chrominance processing channel

It will be recalled that the chrominance information forms part of the composite video from which it has to be separated before demodulation. The chrominance information is centred on a 4.43 MHz subcarrier with a bandwidth limited to ±1 MHz. The first task of the chrominance channel is therefore to separate the chrominance from the composite video. This is carried out by the bandpass chrominance amplifier (Fig. 12.1). Before demodulation can take place, the composite chrominance signal must be separated into its two component parts, $U$ and $V$, each of which must be demodulated separately to recreate the original colour difference signals. The weighted colour difference signals $U$ and $V$ are separated from each other by a unit consisting of a delay line (usually known as PAL delay line) and an add/subtract network. Two separate signals, $U$ and $V$, are produced, which are fed to their respective demodulators, $B' - Y'$ and $R' - Y'$. Each demodulator is fed with a 4.43 MHz signal at the correct phase from the reference oscillator and burst channel. Two gamma-corrected colour difference signals $B' - Y'$ and $R' - Y'$ are thus obtained. The third colour difference signal, $G' - Y'$, is obtained from the first two by the $G' - Y'$ network as shown. The three colour difference signals together with luminance signal, $Y'$, are then fed into the RGB matrix. By adding $Y'$ to the three colour difference signals, the original gamma-corrected $R'$, $G'$ and $B''$ colours are reproduced which, after amplification, are fed directly into the appropriate c.r.t. gun. A luminance delay line is inserted into the luminance signal path to ensure that both signals arrive at the matrix at the same time.

The chrominance channel must also provide a facility for some or all of the following functions:

- Colour kill to turn the chrominance amplifier off during monochrome-only transmission.
- Manual saturation (or colour) control to allow the user to change the colour intensity of the display by varying the gain of the chrominance amplifier.
- Automatic chrominance control, a.c.c., which varies the gain of the chrominance amplifier.

110

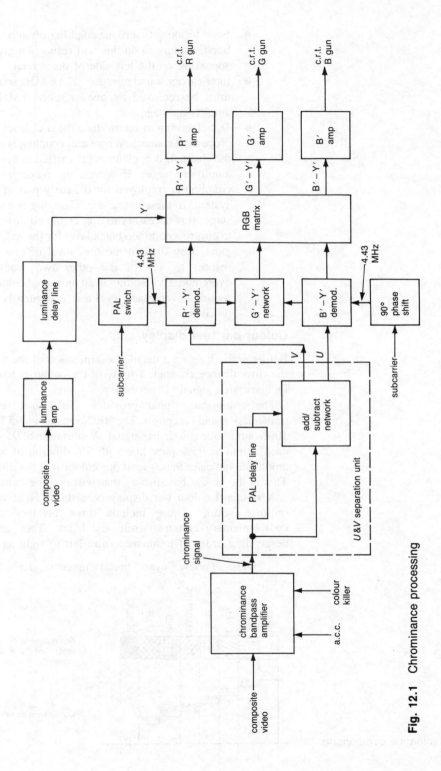

**Fig. 12.1** Chrominance processing

- Burst blanking to turn the amplifier off during the subcarrier burst. Failure to do this will result in a greenish striation appearing on the left side of the screen.
- Inter-carrier sound rejection. The 6 MHz sound inter-carrier must be removed by one or more 6 MHz traps in the amplifying stage.
- D.c clamping to reintroduce the d.c. level lost during the processing channel. Where a.c. coupling is used throughout the channel, d.c. clamping is carried out at the RGB drive amplifier stage. However, in modern receivers d.c. coupling is employed for the early part of the processing system. In these cases, d.c. clamping is used at an earlier stage. It is necessary to d.c. clamp all three colour signals to ensure a common black level for the red, green and blue guns. Any drift in the d.c. level of one amplifier with respect to any of the other two would lead to an overemphasis resulting in an unwanted colour tint. For this reason driven black level d.c. clamping is used in colour receivers.

## Colour-bar test display

Before embarking on a detailed examination of the various parts of the chrominance channel, a study of the colour-bar test display and its associated signals is necessary.

The colour-bar signal provides a rigorous test for colour transmission and reception. The BBC transmits a 95% saturated and 100% amplitude colour-bar signal. A saturation of 95% indicates that each colour is 95% pure hue with 5% dilution of white. A 100% amplitude indicates that at least one colour is at maximum amplitude. This is the colour-bar display that will now be considered.

A standard colour-bar display consists of eight vertical bars of uniform width. These include three primary colours, three complementary colours, white and black. They are arranged in descending order of luminance from left to right as follows:

white    yellow    cyan    green    magenta    red    blue    black

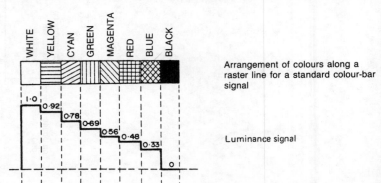

Arrangement of colours along a raster line for a standard colour-bar signal

Luminance signal

**Fig. 12.2** Luminance components of colour bars

A monochrome receiver displays the luminance component of the colour-bar display (Fig. 12.2). This is known as the 'grey scale' with peak white on the left followed by grey stripes which grow progressively darker until black is reached on the right-hand side. It will be seen that luminance steps are not uniform.

The RGB components of the colour-bar display are shown in Fig. 12.3 representing the waveforms at the red, green and blue guns of the cathode ray tube.

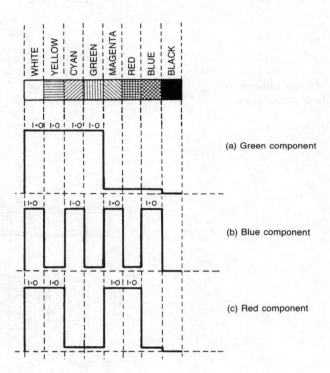

**Fig. 12.3** RGB components of colour bars

The actual components of the chrominance signal, i.e. the colour difference signals, may be calculated by the summation of the amplitude of the various components at each bar. First the RGB signals are gamma-corrected to produce $R'$, $G'$ and $B'$. Then by subtracting each one from the luminance $Y'$, gamma-corrected colour difference signals are obtained. The $B' - Y'$ and $R' - Y'$ colour difference are then weighted to produce $U$ and $V$ respectively as shown in Fig. 12.4. These components are amplitude modulated using two 4.43 MHz quadrature subcarriers. The carrier is then suppressed and the phasors representing the two components are added to produce the complete colour bar chrominance signal shown in Fig. 12.5(a). This chrominance signal is then mounted on the luminance signal in (b) to produce the complete composite video signal for a colour-bar display shown in (c).

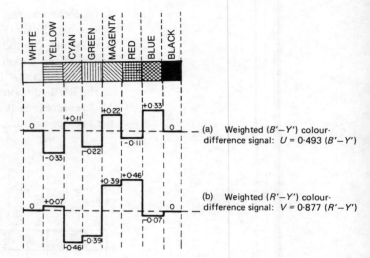

(a)    Weighted $(B'-Y')$ colour-difference signal: $U = 0.493\ (B'-Y')$

(b)    Weighted $(R'-Y')$ colour-difference signal: $V = 0.877\ (R'-Y')$

**Fig. 12.4**    Colour difference components of colour bars

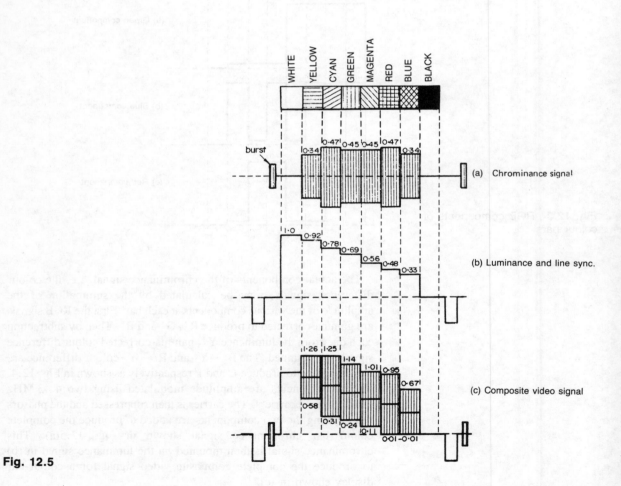

(a) Chrominance signal

(b) Luminance and line sync.

(c) Composite video signal

**Fig. 12.5**

## Chrominance amplifier

The primary function of the chrominance amplifier is to extract the chrominance information from the composite video and amplify it to a level suitable to drive the delay line and the add/subtract network. It is essentially a bandpass amplifier consisting of two or more stages of amplification. A typical two-stage chrominance amplifier used in early colour receivers is shown in Fig. 12.6 in which the tuned pair 2L18/2C47 and 2L19/2C51 with top capacitance coupling 2C50 provide the required bandpass of ±1 MHz. Two RC-coupled amplifiers are used, 2VT8 and 2VT9. Automatic chrominance control is achieved using the principle of reverse a.g.c. by which the gain of the npn transistor 2VT7 is controlled. The a.c.c. control voltage is applied to the emitter of d.c. amplifier 2VT7. The amplified control voltage at the collector of 2VT7 is then applied to the base of 2VT8 via 2L17 to determine its bias and hence its gain. Similarly, adjustment of the colour saturation control 2RV3 causes 2VT8 bias voltage and hence its gain to change accordingly.

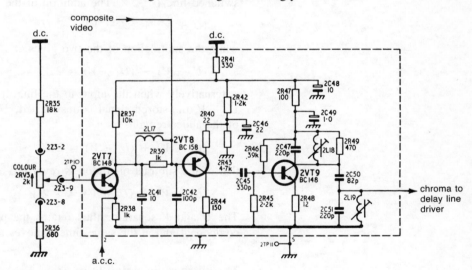

**Fig. 12.6** Two-stage chrominance amplifier (Bush)

## U and V separation

The principle of the PAL-D system of separating the $U$ and $V$ components is shown in Fig. 12.7 in which the chrominance signal of the previous line is stored or delayed for one line duration (64 μs). The delayed signal is then added to and subtracted from the signal of the current line to produce separate $U$ and $V$ signals. The precise value of the required delay is 63.943 μs, which is slightly less than one line duration because it must correspond to a whole number of subcarriers.

Let us assume that the chrominance signal going into the delay line driver in Fig. 12.7 is unswitched, i.e. $U + V$. The chrominance signal

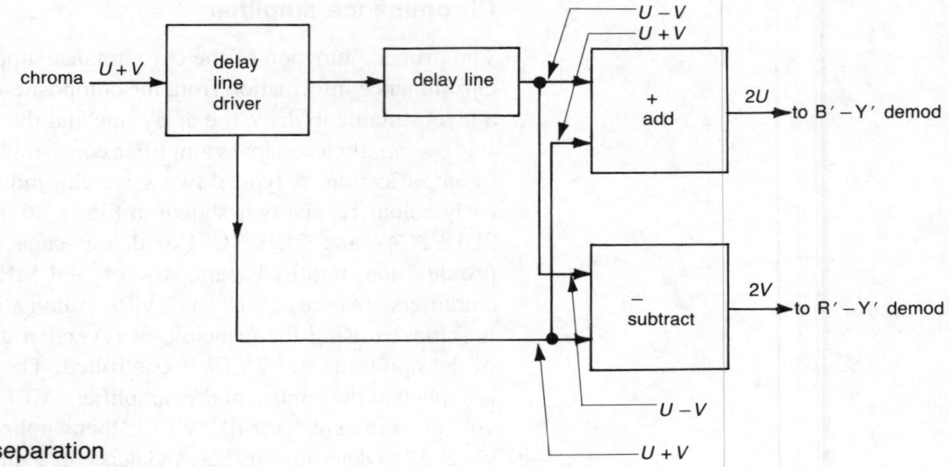

```
                              ┌─────────┐              ┌──────────┐        ╲  U − V
                              │ delay   │              │          │         ╲ U + V
  chroma   U + V              │ line    │              │ delay line│       ┌──────────┐
 ─────────────────────────────│ driver  │───────────────│          │──●──────│   +      │──── 2U
                              └─────────┘              └──────────┘  │   ╱   │  add     │──── to B′ − Y′ demod
                                   │                                │  ╱    └──────────┘
                                   │                                │ ╱
                                   │                                ●        ┌──────────┐
                                   │                                         │   −      │──── 2V
                                   └────────────────────────────────●────────│ subtract │──── to R′ − Y′ demod
                                                                    │        └──────────┘
                                                                    │   ╲   U − V
                                                                     ╲   ╲ U + V
```

**Fig. 12.7** *U* and *V* separation

at the output of the delayed line is that of the preceding line, i.e. switched line $U - V$. The addition of the two signals results in

$$(U + V) + (U - V) = 2\,U$$

while the subtraction of the two gives

$$(U + V) - (U - V) = 2\,V$$

Alternatively when the input to the line driver is a switched line, $U - V$, the stored signal is unswitched, $U + V$. While the result of the adder remains as

$$(U - V) + (U + V) = 2\,U.$$

that of the subtract operation is reversed, as follows

$$(U - V) - (U + V) = -2\,V.$$

The $U$ and $V$ separator thus retains the phase reversal of the $V$ component and at the same time removes the phase error.

## The ultrasonic delay line

To provide the comparatively long delay required by the PAL-D receiver it is not practical to use electrical methods. Instead, ultrasonic delay lines are used in which a transducer converts the electrical signal into an ultrasonic wave which is made to travel along a solid glass block. Another similar transducer at the other end reverses the process and the chrominance signal is recovered. The speed of propagation of ultrasonic waves is about 2750 m/s which is far lower than electric waves in a conductor. Provided a suitable length of the glass block is used (about 17.6 cm) a delay of 64 $\mu$s may be obtained.

An early construction of an ultrasonic delay line is shown in Fig. 12.8 in which a single reflecting surface is used. The length of such a delay line is approximately 8.8 cm (1/2 × 17.6 cm). Modern delay

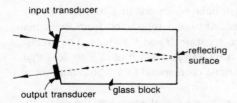

**Fig. 12.8** Ultrasonic delay line

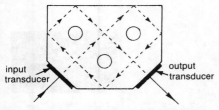

**Fig. 12.9** Multiple surface ultrasonic delay line

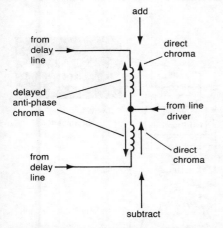

**Fig. 12.10** Add/subtract network

lines employ multiple reflecting surfaces as shown in Fig. 12.9. The required path length is obtained by arranging for the ultrasonic wave to reflect back and forth within the delay line. A delay line with smaller dimensions is therefore possible.

It is essential for the delay time of the line to remain substantially constant at $63.943 \, \mu s$. A specially selected glass is thus used in the manufacture of the delay line.

### *U* and *V* separator circuit

A typical add/subtract network is shown in Fig. 12.10. It consists of a centre-tapped transformer fed with a delayed chrominance signal across its two terminals. Two equal and opposite (anti-phase) delayed chrominance signals thus develop across each half of the transformer winding. The direct (undelayed) chrominance signal is fed into the centre tap so that it adds to the delayed signal in one half (top half) and subtracts from the delayed signal in the other half (bottom half). These two signals are then used to feed the $R' - Y'$ and $B' - Y'$ demodulators respectively.

### Use of integrated circuits

A circuit using the SN76226 chip incorporating a chrominance amplifier and *U-V* separator is shown in Fig. 12.11. The chrominance signal applied to pin 8 of the i.c. is amplified by a two-stage gain controlled amplifier. The gain of the first stage is set by a manual colour or saturation control at pin 7. The gain of the second stage is adjusted by the contrast control applied at pin 16 which also adjusts the gain of the luminance amplifier. The chrominance signal emerges at pin 10 which is the collector of an internal transistor. The gain of this transistor is determined by its emitter resistor connected externally at pin 11. From pin 10, the chrominance is fed to the PAL delay line. The direct signal is taken from L115 via C166 to the centre of the bifilar L119. Amplitude and phase adjustments are provided by R167, L115 and L119. Black level clamping is driven by line pulses applied to pin 5 of the chip. The output from the black level clamp is fed into the base of an internal transistor to provide the necessary d.c. restoration for the luminance signal. The SN76226 also incorporates a sync. separator with line and field pulses appearing at pin 3.

### Colour difference demodulators

The weighted chrominance components *U* and *V* from the separator unit are applied to their individual colour difference demodulators to obtain $B' - Y'$ and $R' - Y'$. The third colour difference signal, $G' - Y'$, is obtained by a $G' - Y'$ matrix as shown in Fig. 12.12. For the $B' - Y'$ demodulator, the subcarrier is shifted by 90° while

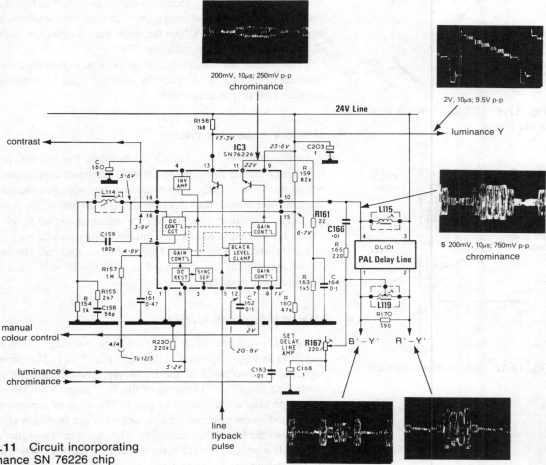

200mV, 10μs; 250mV p-p
chrominance

2V, 10μs; 9.5V p-p

24V Line

luminance Y

contrast

5 200mV, 10μs; 750mV p-p
chrominance

manual
colour control

luminance
chrominance

line
flyback
pulse

100mV, 10μs; 280mV p-p

100mV, 10μs; 400mV p-p

**Fig. 12.11** Circuit incorporating
chrominance SN 76226 chip
(Ferguson 9000)

that for the R′ − Y′ demodulator the subcarrier is phase reversed
every line through the PAL switch.

It will be recalled that the U and V components of the chrominance
signal are the weighted colour difference signals whereby

$$U = 0.493(B' - Y')$$

and

$$V = 0.877(R' - Y')$$

It follows that before B′ − Y′ and R′ − Y′ are recovered, the
weighted components must be de-weighted. This is usually carried
out at the demodulation stage by the inclusion of colour difference
amplifiers which provide the B′ − Y′ channel more gain than the
R′ − Y′ channel. The whole unit is then referred to as the colour
difference (B′ − Y′ or R′ − Y′) demodulator (Fig. 12.13).

In amplitude modulation the information is contained in the change

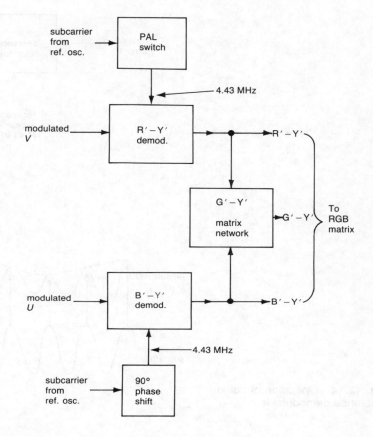

**Fig. 12.12**  Colour difference
processing

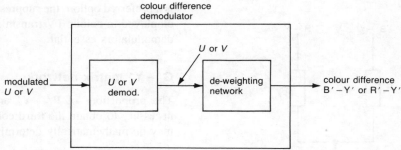

**Fig. 12.13**  Colour difference
demodulation

of the amplitude of the peak of the carrier. When the carrier is suppressed, the modulating information continues to reside in the changing amplitude of the modulated signal. To recover the original information, the amplitude of the modulated signal has to be detected when the carrier is at its peak. In order to do this a synchronous detector is used. In essence the colour difference synchronous demodulator is a switching or sampling device which detects the level of the incoming modulated $U$ (or $V$) signal every time the regenerated subcarrier is at its positive peak as shown in Fig. 12.14.

Unlike video demodulation where the use of synchronous detectors

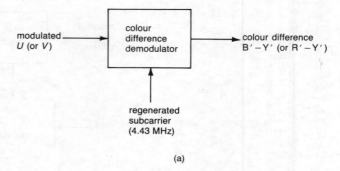

(a)

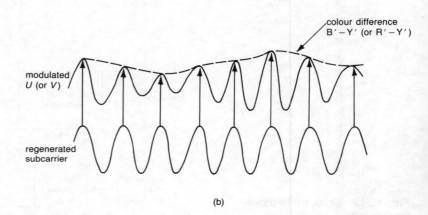

**Fig. 12.14** Operation of colour difference demodulator

(b)

is a preferred option, the suppressed subcarrier amplitude modulation employed in colour TV transmission makes the use of synchronous demodulators essential.

### G′ − Y′ matrix network

The proportions of R′ − Y′ and B′ − Y′ components which are necessary to obtain the third colour difference component G′ − Y′ may be mathematically determined as

$$G' - Y' = 0.51(R' - Y') - 0.186(B' - Y')$$

However, if G′ − Y′ matrixing takes place before de-weighting of the U and V components is carried out, different proportions are necessary, namely

$$G' - Y' = -0.29(R' - Y') - 0.186(B' - Y')$$

Since the required R′ − Y′ and B′ − Y′ levels are both less than unity, they may be derived by using a simple resistor network such as that shown in Fig. 12.15. The ratio of $R_x$, $R_y$ and $R_z$ is chosen to provide the correct proportions of B′ − Y′ and R′ − Y′.

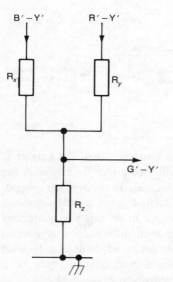

**Fig. 12.15** Simple resistor matrix

## Luminance delay

The next stage of the chrominance processing channel is the addition of the luminance signal to the colour difference signals to obtain the three gamma-corrected primary coloura, R′, G′ and B′. At this point the chrominance and luminance signals must be in step. For this to happen, the time taken by the two signals to pass through their amplifiers and associated circuitry must be equal. The chrominance signal which has a relatively narrow 1 MHz bandwidth suffers a greater delay than the luminance which has a bandwidth of 5.5 MHz. To compensate for this an extra delay has to be introduced into the luminance signal path. A luminance delay of $0.5 - 1.0\,\mu s$ is thus inserted before the luminance is fed into the RGB matrix.

A typical delay consists of a single solenoid wound over earthed metal strips. The cut-off frequency is designed to fall well above the highest luminance frequency and the fall in output at the high-frequency end is compensated for by 'free' metal strips positioned along the coil. The delay line must be properly terminated at each end by its characteristic impedance to avoid reflection of the luminance signal from one end to the other.

The absence of a delay in the luminance signal results in a double image on the screen, one image due to the luminance and the other due to the chrominance signal, an effect similar to ghosting. Multiple images will also be observed if the delay line is not properly terminated.

Modern delay line constructions include an internal 4.43 MHz subcarrier rejector circuit thus dispensing with yet another alignment adjustment at the manufacturing stage.

## RGB matrix

At the tube a picture is produced by modulating the three c.r.t. electron beams by the gamma-corrected R′, G′ and B′ signals. These are derived by the addition of the colour difference signals to the gamma-corrected luminance signals Y′:

$$Y' + (R' - Y') = R'$$
$$Y' + (G' - Y') = G'$$
$$Y' + (B' - Y') = B'$$

The difference in the bandwidth of the luminance signal on one hand and the colour difference signals on the other introduces **glitches** or notches at points of fast colour transitions when the process of addition takes place. The narrow bandwidth of the colour difference signals restricts the rise time of fast changing signals. When added to the corresponding fast changing luminance signal a 'glitch' is introduced as shown in Fig. 12.16. On a colour-bar display the effect of the glitch is displayed as a dark band between the colour bars.

The addition may be carried out by a special matrix before the R′, G′ and B′ colour signals are applied to the cathode of the c.r.t., a

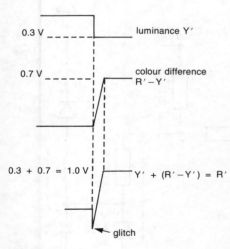

0.3 V ----  luminance Y′

0.7 V ----  colour difference R′−Y′

0.3 + 0.7 = 1.0 V ----  Y′ + (R′−Y′) = R′

glitch

**Fig. 12.16**

technique known as **direct drive**. Alternatively, matrixing may be carried out by the tube itself, a technique known as **colour difference** drive. The latter involves feeding the colour difference signals to the control grids of the c.r.t. while at the same time applying a negative luminance signal, $-Y'$ to the cathodes. Applying a negative luminance to the cathode is equivalent to applying a positive luminance to the grid which results in the mathematical addition of the two signals.

In the colour difference drive, separate colour difference and luminance signals are fed into different electrodes of the c.r.t. This results in problems of timing which are accentuated by the fact that the two signals have different bandwidths, 5.5 MHz for the luminance and 1 MHz for the colour difference. Further problems arise from the relative sensitivities of the electrodes which have to be maintained the same for all levels of the input signals. Direct RGB drive on the other hand overcomes these problems by performing the necessary matrixing close to the point at which demodulation takes place. For these reasons direct RGB drive is used in modern TV receivers.

## Beam limiting

Most TV receivers employ some form of beam current limiting which ensures that the electron emission (beam current) and hence brightness does not exceed a predetermined limit. Beam limiting is optional as far as monochrome receivers are concerned but essential for colour TV applications. A very high beam current overloads the line output

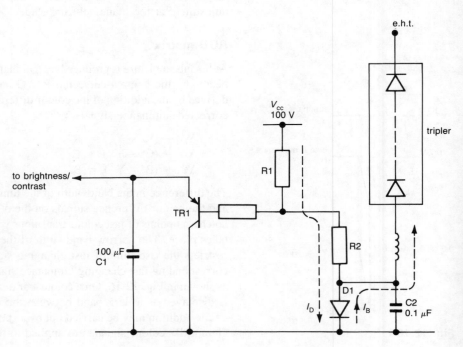

**Fig. 12.17**   Beam limiter

amplifier and the e.h.t. tripler causing deterioration in focus, it overdrives the c.r.t. causing limited highlights and results in excessive power dissipation in the mask within the tube which may cause misconvergence of the three primary colours on the screen.

Beam limiting involves sampling or monitoring the strength of the beam current directly at the cathode or indirectly by monitoring the d.c. current taken at the line output stage or the e.h.t. winding. The beam current itself is then controlled by reducing the black level (i.e. the brightness) or the amplitude of the luminance signal (i.e. the contrast) or both.

The circuit in Fig. 12.17 shows a typical beam limiter arrangement used in colour TV receivers in which the e.h.t. current is monitored by a diode D1 placed between the earthy end of the e.h.t. overwind and chassis. Two types of current flow through D1: forward current $I_D$ of about $600\,\mu A$ to chassis caused by voltage $V_{cc}$ and beam current $I_B$ flowing in the opposite direction. When the beam current goes above $600\,\mu A$, D1 switches off and its anode goes negative which reduces the base voltage of emitter follower TR1 and hence varies the brightness/contrast controls. For larger tubes the preset beam current limiting is raised to $1\,mA$. C1 and C2 are decoupling capacitors.

## Video output stage

With RGB drive the output stage must be able to deliver a peak-to-peak signal of between $80-150\,V$ to the c.r.t. cathode. The signal drive to each gun is different because of the different efficiencies of the electrodes with the red gun requiring the largest drive. The large signal drive requires a high d.c. supply voltage and often two transistors are connected in series to share this high voltage. To ensure adequate bandwidth, series peaking coils may be employed. Power transistors in class A configuration are used with the necessary heat sinks to deliver the relatively large power necessary to drive the red, green and blue guns of the c.r.t. A small load resistance or an emitter follower buffer are used to ensure low output impedance. This low impedance allows for fast charge and discharge of the c.r.t.'s cathode input impedance to give good frequency response at the upper end of the bandwidth.

Output stages are normally mounted on the c.r.t. base panel to remove the bandwidth limitations associated with long leads.

Early output stages were also used for matrixing by feeding the luminance to the base and the colour difference signal to the emitter of the transistor. Black level clamping and brightness control of the three guns were also incorporated at the video output stage as well as grey scale adjustment. The purpose of grey scale adjustment or **tracking** is to ensure that a purely monochrome picture has no traces of colour tint at any level of brightness from lowlights to highlights across the grey scale display. With the introduction of more advanced

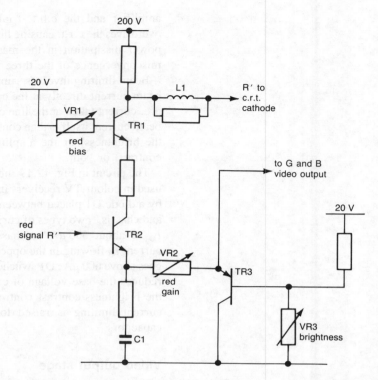

**Fig. 12.18** Video output stage

integrated circuits, matrixing is now carried out separately and clamping is introduced at the luminance signal channel before matrixing.

Modern integrated circuits provide complete luminance and colour processing on a single chip including such functions as blanking, black level clamping, beam limiting, and brightness and contrast control. RGB buffer amplifiers are also included to provide large colour drives (about 3 V) for the output stages. Some i.c.s include automatic grey scale correction.

The essential elements of a video output stage suitable for driving a precision-in-line (PIL) tube is shown in Fig. 12.18. Only the red stage is shown since the other two stages are identical. TR1 and TR2 are connected in cascode to share the 200 V d.c. supply and to provide the necessary controls of the output signal: the bias control VR1 which determines the cut-off point of the gun (lowlights) and the gain control VR2 which controls the highlights. The bias control is necessary since the A1 electrodes in a PIL tube are strapped together and must be adjusted at the video stage. The base voltage of TR1 is set by VR1 which determines the collector potential and hence the potential of the red cathode. TR2 is driven by the red signal R′ from a preceding i.c. which also provides the d.c. base bias voltage. The gain of TR2 is set by VR2 which varies the d.c. current and hence the gain of the amplifier. This control together with similarly located preset resistors in the green and blue output stages are used to set the

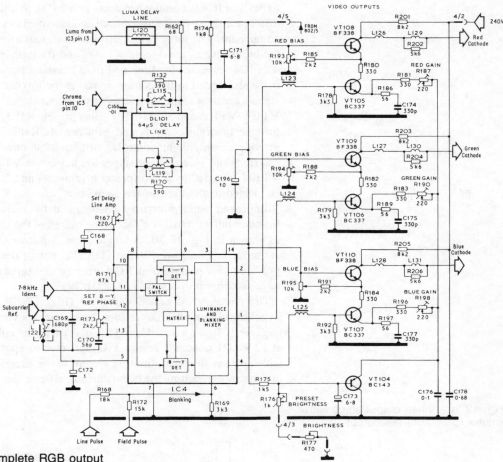

**Fig. 12.19**  Complete RGB output stage (Ferguson 9000 chassis)

individual drives of the three guns when carrying out the grey scale highlight corrections. TR3 provides the path for the TR2 d.c. current. By changing VR3, the current through the TR2 and TR1 is varied and with it the red cathode potential. Since TR3 also forms the d.c. path for the green and blue cascode arrangements, VR3 causes the d.c. potential of the three cathodes to vary together thus providing brightness control. High frequency response is maintained by peaking series coil L1 at the output. VR2 and TR3 provide negative feedback for low and medium frequencies. High frequencies are decoupled via C1 to maintain the gain at the upper end.

A practical circuit employing cascode output stages is shown in Fig. 12.19 in which IC4 (SN76227) provides $R' - Y'$ and $B' - Y'$ demodulation, $G' - Y'$ matrixing, RGB matrixing and blanking. The chrominance signal is fed to the chroma delay line DL101 and subsequently split into $B' - Y'$ and $R' - Y'$ by bifilar L119 and fed to pins 8 and 9 of IC4 respectively. Amplitude and phase adjustments are provided by R167, L115 and L119. The luminance signal is fed to pin 3 of IC4 via luminance delay line L120. Within IC4 the colour difference signals are demodulated and matrixed to yield the $G' - Y'$ component. The three colour difference signals are then mixed with the luminance to provide the $R'$, $G'$ and $B'$ signals at pins 2, 1 and 4 of IC4 respectively. Line and field blanking pulses applied at pin 6 are also added to the colour signals at the mixing stage. The RGB signals are then fed to their respective output stages: VT108/VT105, VT109/VT106 and VT110/107. Bias presets R193, R194 and R195 provide lowlight controls and gain presets R187, R190 and R198 provide the highlight controls. Brightness control is achieved by returning the video output stages to chassis via VT104. The bias of VT104 is varied by R176 (preset brightness) and R177 (brightness) connected to the base of the transistor.

Improved bandwidth may be obtained by including an emitter follower buffer transistor TR2 at the output of the video output stage as shown in Fig. 12.20. A single class A transistor amplifier TR1 is used in conjunction with the TDA3301 colour decoder chip which provides a 3 V peak-to-peak RGB drive for the output transistors which have maximum dissipation of 400 mW.

The circuitry associated with TR3 (Fig. 12.20) is a **slow start** switching circuit which overrides the system at switch on. When the receiver is first switched on, TR3 is off with its collector potential at 12 V. D1 conducts taking TR2 collector to approximately 12 V which causes the beam limiting system in the decoder chip to come into operation, cutting the beam current. After a short period of time

**Fig. 12.20** Video output stage with emitter follower at the output

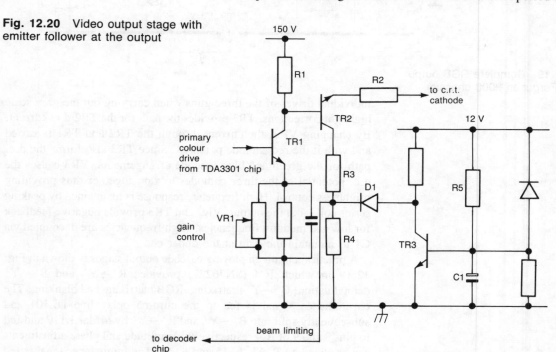

(determined by time constant C1R5), capacitor C1 charges up through R5 and when it reaches a certain level, TR3 turns on bringing its collector down to chassis potential. D1 is now reverse biased isolating TR3 from the rest of the circuit and releasing the beam current. The potential at the junction of R3/R4 is fed to decoder chip TDA3301 for the purpose of normal beam limiting. As the beam current increases, the potential at R3/R4 junction increases which is then used to set the contrast control accordingly. TR3 is also included to avoid a peak white flash caused by the automatic grey scale adjusment produced by the processor chip during the heater warm-up period.

## Automatic grey scale correction

Automatic grey scale correction is carried out by clamping the three beams: R, G and B. The clamp levels are set up individually by comparing the beam current level of each gun with an internal reference generated by a timing and logic counter. The error voltages produced are stored for each individual gun. A switched sampling system is used which carries out the process of comparison and storage for each beam current in turn. A scanner then adjusts the luminance signal for each beam before it is fed to the matrix. This system corrects the lowlight drive levels only. The highlights are corrected in the traditional way by adjusting the gain of the red and green output amplifiers. Following normal practice, the gain of the blue channel is fixed at close to maximum.

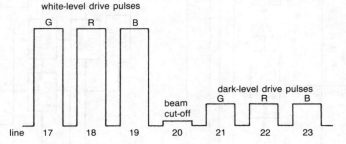

**Fig. 12.21** Automatic grey scale drive pulses

Automatic grey scale tracking is carried out during the field blanking period. In the HA11498 processing chip automatic grey scale tracking drive pulses are inserted on blanked lines 17 to 23 as shown in Fig. 12.21. Green, red and blue white-level pulses (highlights) are inserted on lines 17, 18 and 19 respectively while dark-level pulses (lowlights) are inserted on lines 21, 22 and 23 respectively with line 20 reserved for a beam cut-off test pulse. In each case the drive current for each gun is measured in sequence and set to the appropriate level.

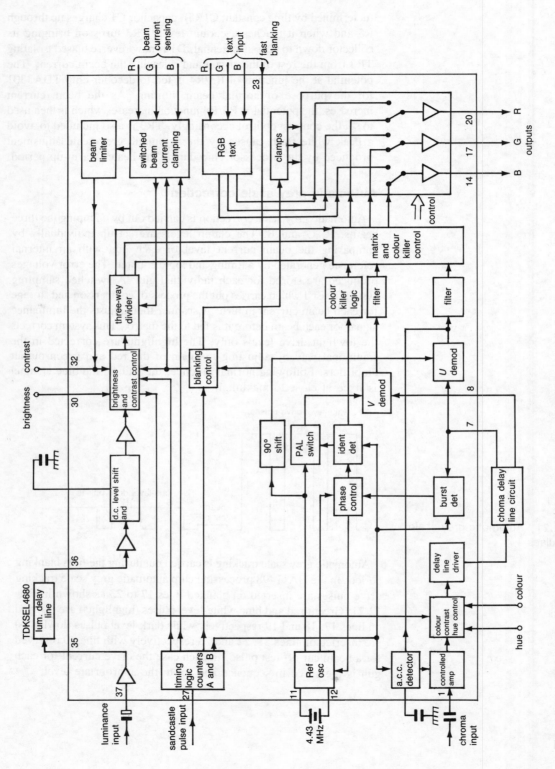

**Fig. 12.22** TDA 3301 colour processing chip and associate circuitry

The luminance signal is first amplified within the i.c. before emerging at pin 35 to pass through the luminance delay line package. It re-enters the chip at pin 36. The luminance delay line represents a thick film circuit and includes the subcarrier rejecter. Internal systems operating on the luminance channel perform black-level clamping, contrast control and blanking. The contrast and saturation controls are interlinked. The effect of the brightness control at pin 30 is to shift the d.c. level on which the luminance signal sits. A preset brightness control is also provided.

The chrominance circuitry follows conventional practice. The reference oscillator is tuned to 4.43 MHz and the 90° phase shift is carried out within the i.c. After filtering, the colour difference signals are matrixed with the luminance signal. The blanking signals are inserted at this stage. Two timing and logic counters A and B are employed to extract blanking, clamping and burst gate pulses from the sandcastle pulse input.

The 'switched beam current clamping' unit provides the control voltage for beam limiting. When the current for any of the three beams reaches the maximum allowable value, the 'beam limiter' reduces the drive via the contrast control.

The chip provides for a changeover to direct RGB video text input. The changeover is controlled by the 'fast blanking' at pin 23 which operates the switching arrangements at the ouput amplifier stage.

## The TDA3301 colour processing chip

One of the most comprehensive colour decoder chips is the 40-pin TDA3301 shown in Fig. 12.22. It incorporates automatic grey scale correction to ease colour balance adjustment during manufacture and provide compensation as the tube ages.

# 13 Power supply circuits

The various sections of the TV receiver demand different power requirements depending on their function and the level of the signal that is being handled. Large-amplitude signals from the video and the line output stages require a high or boost voltage of between 150−250 V known as high tension, h.t. On the other hand, a low voltage supply of between 10−40 V sometimes known as low tension, l.t., is required for those sections such as the tuner, the i.f. strip, video or sound drive and field or line oscillators that handle small signal levels. Furthermore extra high tension, e.h.t., in the region of 25 kV is necessary for the final anode of the cathode ray tube.

Apart from the a.c. supply to the tube's heater and d.c. supplies to the field and line oscillators, regulated power supplies are necessary to ensure steady output levels. The power supply must also ensure safe operation of the receiver under normal conditions as well as under faulty conditions such as excessive current or voltage requirements. A great diversity of approaches and techniques are employed in the design of power supplies for TV receivers. The aim is to improve regulation and efficiency and to minimise power dissipation, thus reducing the cost and weight of the receiver.

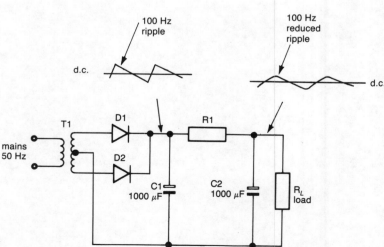

**Fig. 13.1**  Unregulated power supply

## Unregulated power supply

A simple unregulated power supply is shown in Fig. 13.1 in which D1-D2 is a mains full-wave rectifier. C1 is a reservoir capacitor and R1C2 is a smoothing or low-pass filter which removes the 100 Hz ripple appearing at the output. For a more effective smoothing, the series resistor R1 may be replaced by a large inductor. In this simple circuit the d.c. output decreases as the load current increases. For a constant d.c. output, a regulator or a stabiliser must be used. It is essential that the d.c. output is maintained constant against both changes in the mains supply (**mains regulation**) and changes in the load current (**load regulation**).

## Series stabilisation

A simple series stabiliser or regulator is shown in Fig. 13.2 in which TR1 is the series regulator. Load regulation is obtained by zener diode Z1 which provides the reference voltage for the base of common emitter transistor TR1. Z1 maintains the base of TR1 at a constant potential determined by its breakdown voltage. The d.c. output taken at the emitter is thus maintained at 0.6 V below the zener voltage. Changes in the output level result in changes in the b-e bias of the series stabiliser in such a way as to keep the output constant.

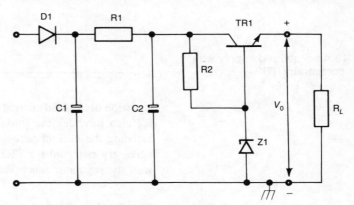

**Fig. 13.2** A series stabilised power supply

For higher load currents, a Darlington pair may be used as shown in Fig. 13.3. Both transistors are connected in the emitter follower configuration with an overall gain equal to the product of the gain of each transistor. A Darlington pair i.c. package is normally used.

The sensitivity of the regulator may be improved by the incorporation of a voltage comparator also known as an **error detector** as shown in Fig. 13.4. TR1 is the normal series regulator. TR2 compares a portion of the output voltage with the reference voltage of the zener. Changes in the output level are amplified and fed into the base of TR1 which maintains the output constant. A shunt bypass resistor, R2, is sometimes connected across the c-e junction of TR1 to reduce the power dissipation of the series stabiliser by diverting

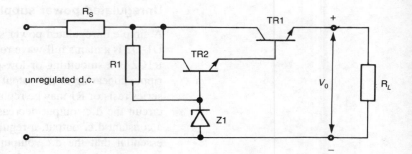

**Fig. 13.3**  Darlington pair stabiliser

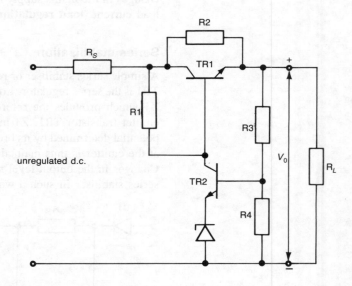

**Fig. 13.4**  Stabilised supply with error comparator TR2

a portion of the load current away from the transistor. Shunt resistor R2 also provides the initial start-up voltage for the regulator by bleeding the current across TR1 to the output which provides the necessary potential for TR2 and the zener to begin to conduct and start the regulator functioning.

## Practical regulated power supply

A regulated power supply used in a monochrome receiver is shown in Fig. 13.5 in which VT21 is the series regulator and VT22 is the comparator or regulator control amplifier. The receiver provides for a battery operation option. The power supply provides a d.c. rail at a nominal value of 11.6 V when the receiver is connected to the mains. W7-W8 is a full-wave rectifier, C88 and C89 are diode bypass capacitors and C85, C86 and C87 are smoothing capacitors. W6 is a protection diode which causes the fuse to blow if the battery is connected the wrong way round.

Zener diode W17 is connected to the h.t. rail with R102 providing its breakdown current. This method reduces the voltage rating of

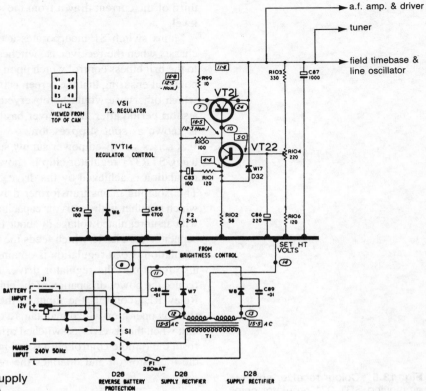

**Fig. 13.5** Regulated power supply
(Ferguson 1590 mono chassis)

comparator VT22 and provides current limitation and s/c protection.
A fall in the h.t. rail due to an increase in load current is compensated
for by increased conduction of the regulator VT21. The circuit
continues to operate in this way until the load current reaches such
a level that the output voltage falls to or below the breakdown voltage
of the zener. At such current levels, the zener ceases to conduct
reducing the voltage across R102 and hence VT22 emitter to almost
chassis potential. With the base of VT22 at a certain positive voltage,
VT22 bottoms saturating VT21 as well. VT21 current is now at its
maximum value thus limiting the load current. This maximum current
continues to flow so long as the output voltage is high enough to
provide the necessary forward bias to the base of VT22. If the output
voltage falls below that level as in the case of a s/c for example, VT22
base drops to zero potential, turning VT22 off which in turn switches
VT21 off and protects the regulator.

The ripple which is present at the input of the regulator is fed to
the emitter of VT22 via phase shift network C83/R101. The phase
shift network ensures that the ripple at the emitter is equal in amplitude
but out of phase with the ripple present there as a result of the feedback
from the output to VT22 base via resistor chain R103/R104/R106.
R99 is a regulator shunt resistor which bypasses approximately one

third of the current drawn from the supply and R104 sets the output level.

Mains switch S1 incorporates a contact which is shorted to the chassis when the receiver is switched off. This contact is connected to the brightness control which upon switching off is taken to chassis potential ensuring that the screen is blacked removing the bright spot which otherwise would be observed in the centre of the screen for a short period after the receiver has been switched off. This process is known as **spot suppression**.

A series stabilised power supply suitable for a colour TV receiver using STR371 regulator chip is shown in Fig. 13.6. Within the i.c., regulation is achieved by the drive controlling the series regulator. The isolating mains transformer drives a full-wave rectifier D1-D4 which together with reservoir capacitor C1 provides the regulator chip with an unregulated voltage of about 135 V. This input voltage charges capacitor C2 via R1 which feeds the regulator drive to ensure mains regulation. Load regulation is obtained by the error amplifier which also feeds into the regulator drive. R3 is a bypass resistor used to reduce the power dissipation of the chip and L1/C3 is a low-pass filter. Relay RL1 controls the input to the full-wave rectifier to provide standby operation which maintains a d.c. supply to the remote control unit when the receiver is switched off. The standby command voltage from the remote control chip is fed into the base of TR1 which turns the transistor on and operates the relay.

**Fig. 13.6** Colour receiver supply employing SRT 371 regulator chip

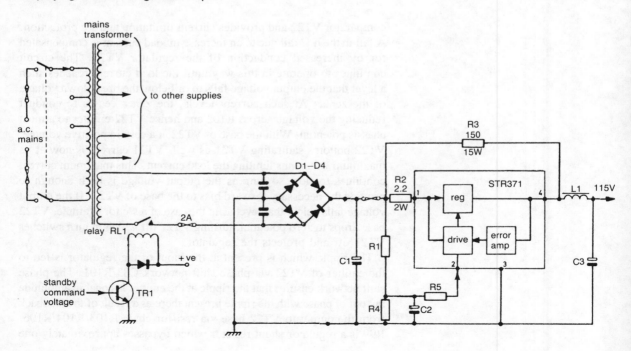

## Thyristor controlled rectifier

It will be recalled that the thyristor (Fig. 13.7) may be triggered into conduction by a positive voltage applied to its gate provided that its anode is positive with respect to the cathode. When fed with an a.c. voltage, the thyristor can only conduct during the positive half cycle. The conduction period is determined by the timing of the trigger pulse to the gate. The output level may thus be controlled by switching the thyristor for longer or shorter periods of time as shown in Fig. 13.8.

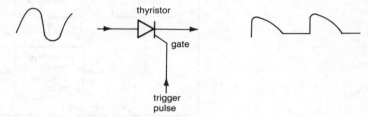

**Fig. 13.7**   The thyristor

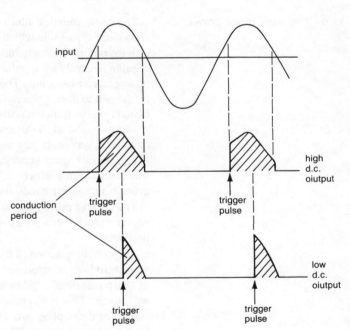

**Fig. 13.8**   Controlled conduction of thyristor

## Switching mode power supplies (SMPS)

The switching mode power supply is in essence a converter. It converts unregulated d.c. into a switched or pulsating d.c. and back again into a regulated d.c. The switching speed determines the a.c. or ripple frequency at the output. There are a variety of switched power supplies in use in TV receivers. They range from the chopper type and the Syclops to the self oscillating power supply, SOPS.

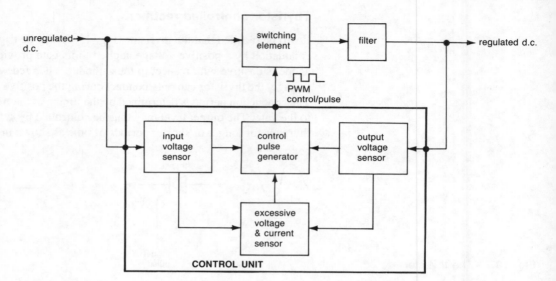

**Fig. 13.9** Switched mode power supply

The basic function blocks of a switched mode power supply are shown in Fig. 13.9 in which the switching element may be a transistor or a thyristor. The switching element which is opened and closed at regular intervals by a pulse from the control unit is used to charge up a reservoir capacitor. The charge across the capacitor is determined by the period during which the switch is closed. Regulation is obtained by making the time intervals when the switching element is open and closed (i.e. the mark-to-space ratio of the control pulse) dependent on the d.c. output. It may also be made dependent on the input voltage to compensate against changes in the mains (or battery) supply voltage. The control unit which is normally an integrated circuit provides protection against excessive current and voltage as shown.

The control pulse generator is in essence a pulse-width modulator which may be driven by line sync. pulses or by a free running oscillator.

The switching action of the SMPS which may involve large currents may introduce interference known as **mains pollution** in the form of sharp transients, spikes or glitches superimposed upon the mains waveform. This is overcome by the introduction of high-frequency chokes or decoupling capacitors at the input terminals which prevent high-frequency pulses from going back into the mains supply.

## The use of the energy reservoir inductor

The switching element which provides control and hence regulation is only one requirement of the switched mode power supply. The other requirement is the efficient use of energy and this is achieved by the use of an inductor as an energy reservoir. The inductor may be connected either in series or in parallel with the load.

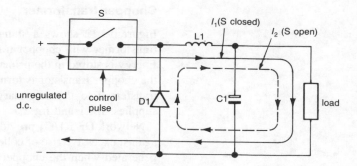

**Fig. 13.10** Series type SMPS

A series connection is shown in Fig. 13.10 in which D1 acts as an efficiency diode. When the switching element S is closed, current $I_1$ flows from the positive side of the unregulated input into the load as shown. The magnetic field set up by the current flowing through L1 causes energy to be stored in the inductor. When the switch is open, the current ceases and the magnetic field collapses. A back e.m.f. is induced across the inductor in such a way as to forward bias D1 causing a current $I_2$ to flow into the load in the same direction as previously. The energy stored in the inductor when the switch was closed is therefore consumed when the switch is open. The ripple at the output has a frequency which is twice the switching speed and is easily removed by smoothing capacitor C1.

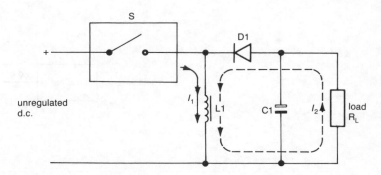

**Fig. 13.11** Shunt type SMPS

A shunt type switched mode power supply is shown in Fig. 13.11. When the switch S is closed, D1 is reverse biased and current $I_1$ flows into L1 feeding energy into the inductor. When the switch is open, $I_1$ collapses and the back e.m.f. across the coil drives current $I_2$ into RL transferring the stored energy from the inductor to the load. One disadvantage of this technique is that since the current flows into the load during the 'open' period of the switch, the output ripple is larger in amplitude and lower in frequency compared with the series connection. However, the parallel connection technique makes it possible to achieve electrical isolation by simply replacing the inductor with a transformer.

## Chopper transformer

Figure 13.12 shows a shunt type power supply using a chopper transformer with chopper transistor TR1 as the switching element. Energy is stored in the primary winding L1 when TR1 is on. When the chopper transistor is turned off, energy stored in the primary is transferred to the secondary windings to produce two regulated supplies: h.t.1 and h.t.2.

Network D3/R1/C1 provides protection for the chopper transistor against excessive rise of collector voltage caused by the back e.m.f. generated when the chopper transistor switches off. When TR1 is turned off, its collector voltage rises turning D3 on. This effectively places C1, known as a '**snubbing**' capacitor, across TR1 which diverts the major part of the back e.m.f. energy away from the transistor. When TR1 is switched on, C1 is discharged through R1.

The use of a chopper transformer makes it possible to obtain a number of regulated d.c. rails by merely adding windings to the transformer as shown in Fig. 13.12. There is thus no need for a mains isolating transformer which saves on the cost and weight of the receiver.

It is normal to derive the control pulse going into the base of TR1 from the line sync. pulse. This makes the functions of the chopper transistor and the line output transistor very similar. This similarity

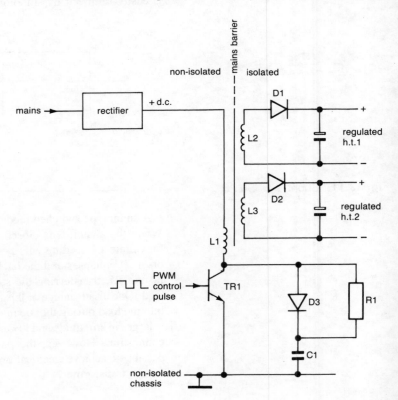

**Fig. 13.12** The use of chopper transformer

prompted some manufacturers to combine the functions of both into a single transistor, a technique known as **Synchronous Converter** and **Line output Stage**, **Syclops**. Other techniques involve combining the functions of the chopper transformer and the line output transformer, into a single transformer a technique known as **IPSALO**, **integrated power supply and line output**.

### Start-up and soft start

Both the switching element and the control unit require a d.c. supply before they can begin to function. Such a voltage may be obtained from the nominal 12 V regulated supply for the control unit or other regulated or unregulated h.t. rails. It is normal that once the control chip is brought into operation, the SMPS itself is used to provide the required regulated voltage to the chip. A slow or soft start is desirable for the switching element to prevent it from overworking at switch-on when the output voltage of the SMPS is zero. Soft start also ensures that the auto-degaussing is completed before the tube starts to be scanned.

### Series chopper SMPS

The basic arrangement for a series chopper power supply is shown in Fig. 13.13 in which D2 is an efficiency diode and L1 acts as the reservoir inductor. Rectified mains is fed to the collector of the chopper transistor TR1. Control pulses from the oscillator are fed to the e−b junction of TR1 via driver TR2 and transformer T1. The oscillator may be a monostable driven by line sync. pulses. This means that the power supply may only start when the line oscillator is made operational. To overcome this disadvantage, a free running oscillator may be used which ensures that the system is self starting. Line pulses may still be used for synchronous operation. The mark-to-space ratio of the control pulse, i.e. the time TR1 is on compared with the time it is off, is determined by the pulse width modulator. Regulation is

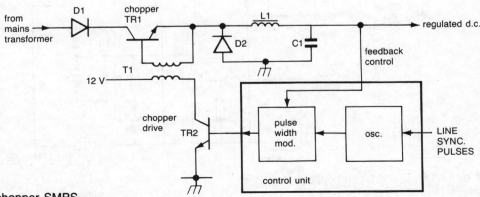

**Fig. 13.13**  Series chopper SMPS

achieved by the feedback control voltage which varies the mark-to-space ratio to compensate for changes in the output voltage. The control chip also includes mains regulation, excessive voltage and current protection, a slow start and standby facility to provide the d.c. supply for the remote control board when the receiver is switched off.

## Shunt type chopper SMPS

Figure 13.14 shows the essential elements for a shunt type switched mode power supply. The shunt chopper transistor TR6 is controlled by TEA2018A chip. Three separate rails are derived from the chopper transformer: 13 V for the line driver and audio stages, 17 V regulated supply and for the signal processing sections of the receiver and 95 V for the line and field output stages. The transformer also provides isolation as shown.

Bridge rectifier D3-D6 together with reservoir capacitor C69 provides the start up voltage for the control chip and the d.c. supply for the chopper transistor. At switch on, C71 charges up from the rectified mains via resistor network R60/R89/R91. When the voltage

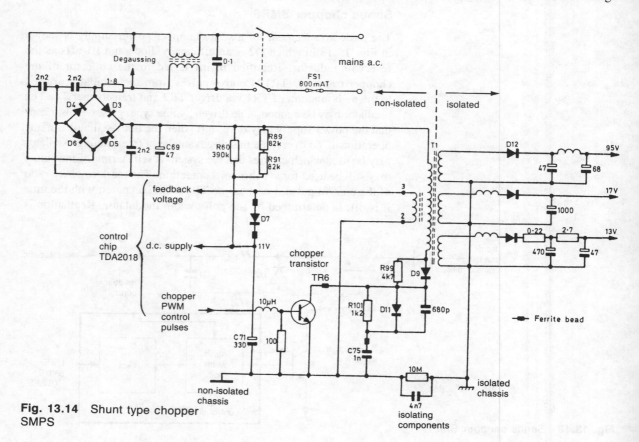

**Fig. 13.14** Shunt type chopper SMPS

across C71 reaches 5.8 V the i.c. swings into operation and delivers drive pulses to the base of the chopper transistor. The transformer is energised and a voltage develops across secondary winding 2-3 which is then rectified by D7 to establish the normal chopper-derived 11 V supply for the control chip. The voltage provided by secondary winding 2-3 is also used to provide the feedback voltage to the control chip. The mark-to-space ratio of the chopper drive pulses is then adjusted by the chip to keep the output constant.

Network C75, R101 and D11 provides protection of TR6 against excessive back e.m.f. Further protection of the transistor is provided by limiting network D9 and R99 which prevents excessive ringing in the transformer due to the back e.m.f.

## Thyristor controlled SMPS

A switched mode power supply using thyristor SR1 as the series switching element is shown in Fig. 13.15 in which L65 is the reservoir inductor, W77 is the efficiency diode and C147 is the reservoir capacitor. To ensure that SCR1 is turned off before W77 comes on, the thyristor cathode is connected to a tapping point on the inductor L65 as shown. The rectified mains is used to charge C137 to about 28 V via potential divider R165/R162. As a result, C138 begins to charge up (via R168) with its bottom plate negative. When this voltage

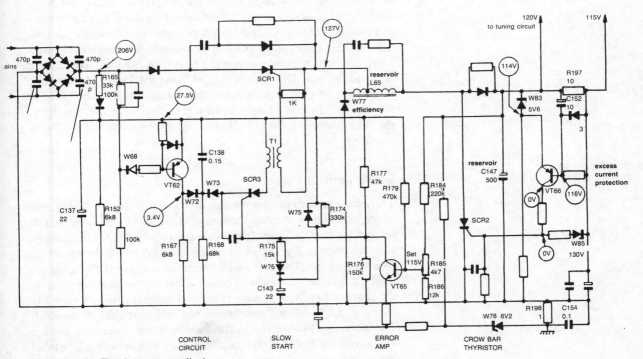

**Fig. 13.15** Thyristor controlled SMPS (Ferguson TX9 chassis)

is less than that at the gate of SCR3, W73 and consequently SCR3 switch on to drive a trigger pulse to the regulator via transformer T1. At the end of each half cycle, the cathode of W68 goes to 0 V. With its anode at a positive potential, W68 conducts, switching VT62 on for a very brief period and discharges C138 ready for the next half cycle. Regulation is obtained by varying the voltage at the gate of driving thyristor SCR3 which varies the firing time of regulator SCR1. Error amplifier VT65 compares a portion of the output voltage fed into its base via R184/5/6 with a reference voltage at its emitter produced by zener W78. Its collector is then used to control the firing of SCR3. Mains regulation is obtained by feeding the voltage developed across C137 to the base of error amplifier VT65 via resistor R179.

C143 provides a slow start facility. At switch on, C143 starts to charge up via R175 and R177. The values of these two resistors are such that SCR3 cannot conduct at the start. As the capacitor charges up, the voltage to the gate of SCR3 rises, firing the SCR first late in the cycle then moving progressively earlier as the voltage across C1434 builds up. This results in a gradual rise in the h.t. voltage. When normal operation of the power supply has been established, the charge across C143 reverse biases W76 thus isolating the slow start network from the rest of the circuit.

Excess voltage protection is provided by the '**crow bar**' action of SCR2. Should the voltage exceed the breakdown voltage of zener W85, SCR2 conducts, taking the cathode of regulator SCR1 to chassis and blowing the fuse. Excess current protection is provided by VT66. Should the current consumption of the receiver rise beyond its normal level, the voltage across smoothing resistor R197 increases causing VT66 to conduct. This fires SCR2 and blows the fuse. VT66 conducts when its base voltage falls below the voltage set by zener W83 at the emitter. To avoid false alarms due to flash-overs of transients, the time constant of R197-C152 is chosen to introduce a delayed response.

## SMPS control chip

There are a number of control chips used in TV receivers. The precise interconnections with other sections of the receiver vary between one set and another. A simplified block diagram of TDA 2582 control chip is shown in Fig. 13.16 in which the oscillator is driven by the line sync. pulse. The pulse-width modulator controls the space-to-mark ratio in such a way as to ensure a constant voltage output from the chopper supply. A remote standby command voltage to pin 4 in excess of 5.6 V will trip the control chip and switch the chopper off. The receiver will then rest in the standby mode. Excessive voltage and current protection as well as soft start are also provided. The trend in i.c. technology is to move to an ever greater degree of integration with a variety of functions being included in a single chip. The functions performed by the power control chip may be incorporated

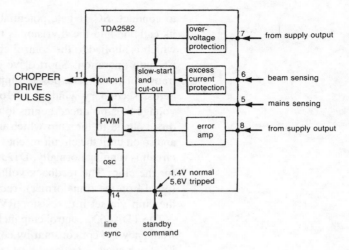

**Fig. 13.16** SMPS control chip

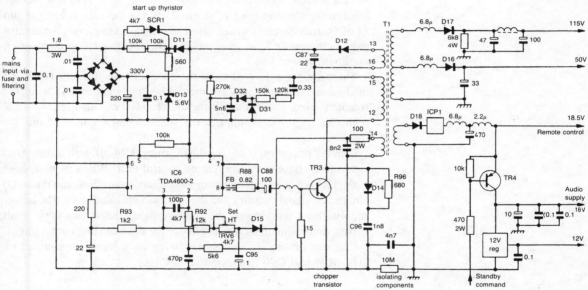

**Fig. 13.17** Switched mode power supply based on TDA 4600 chip (Ferguson TX99 chassis)

into a comprehensive power processor chip which includes line and field processing.

A complete SMPS circuit based on the Siemens TDA4600 control chip is shown in Fig. 13.17, in which TR3 is a shunt type chopper transistor. The bridge rectifier produces a d.c. voltage of about 350 V from the mains input which provides the supply voltage to the chopper transistor.

The start up voltage is provided by thyristor SCR1 and associated circuitry. When the receiver is switched off, C87 is fully discharged and the cathode of SCR1 is at 0 V. At switch on, the a.c. mains are applied to the anode of the thyristor. Clipping zener D13 maintains SCR1 cathode at just under 5.6 V. D11 is reversed biased and the thyristor is turned on charging C87 during the positive half cycles of the input. When the voltage across C87 reaches 6.5 V, D11 begins to conduct. SCR1 gate potential is now slightly lower than that of its cathode and the thyristor is turned off. The voltage across C87 which is applied to the control chip at pin 9 is sufficient to bring the i.c. into operation. Short drive pulses are delivered to the chopper transistor to start the power supply operating. The pulses appearing across secondary winding 13-16 are rectified by D12 and the d.c. voltage thus produced begins to charge C87. This provides a higher d.c. voltage to the chip which in turn produces larger drive pulses and so on until the circuit reaches normal operation. Once the chopper circuit is running normally, D12 and C87 provide a stable 12 V supply for the chip. The feedback voltage is taken across a small winding (pin 14 on the transformer), rectified by D15 and fed into pin 3 of the chip via set h.t. resistor RV6.

The TDA4600 control chip includes a free running oscillator whose frequency is kept constant by components connected to pin 1 of the i.c. Each cycle is initiated by a 'zero-crossing' or a 'zero flux' sensor incorporated within the i.c. at pin 2. When the a.c. voltage at pin 14 of the transformer crosses zero and attempts to reverse, the control chip switches TR3 on to commence the next cycle thus ensuring minimum power loss.

Three rails are derived from the chopper transformer, 115 V for the line output stage, 50 V for the field output stage and 18 V for the remote control and the audio signal. This last rail also feeds a 12 V regulator chip which supplies the small signal sections of the TV receiver.

Standby operation is obtained by turning TR4 off with a command signal to its base from the remote control unit. When its base goes high, TR4 being an npn transistor switches off, thus disabling the audio circuit, the signal circuitry and the line and field oscillators. The power supply keeps working in the standby mode delivering very small current and maintaining the supplies to the field and line output stages.

Chopper protection against excessive back e.m.f is provided by D14, R96 and C96 connected across TR3.

## Syclops

The Synchronous Converter and Line Output Stage, Syclops, developed by Ferguson combines the functions of the chopper and the line output into a single transistor. The basic elements of the Syclops circuit is shown in Fig. 13.18. The chopper/line output transistor TR1 feeds the normal chopper transformer and a standard line-scan/line-output transformer circuit via switching diodes D1 and D2 respectively. As was described in Chapter 9 at time $t_1$ on the scan waveform in Fig. 13.19, TR1 is turned off to start the flyback. Its collector potential goes high switching D1 off. Tuned circuit C1/C2/L1 is pulsed into oscillation. At the end of the flyback, time $t_2$ when the oscillation reaches its negative peak and current begins to change direction, D3 conducts which reverse biases D2 and effectively places C2 across L1 to commence the first part of the scan. At time $t_3$, TR1 is turned on, its collector voltage drops switching D1 on. Current

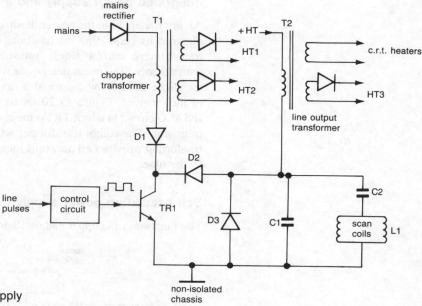

**Fig. 13.18**  Syclops power supply

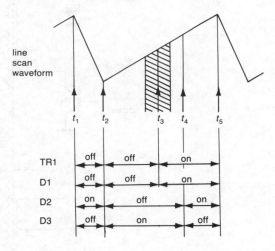

**Fig. 13.19**

begins to flow into the primary winding of the chopper transformer from the mains rectifier causing energy to be stored into T1. At time $t_4$, half way along the scan when the current in the scan coils begins to reverse, D3 is turned off and D2 being forward biased is turned on. TR1 takes over from D3 to complete the second half of the scan. By varying the time at which TR1 is turned on, i.e. by advancing or delaying time instant $t_3$ (shaded area), the energy supplied to the chopper transformer is varied and with it the d.c. output. This has no effect on the scan waveform since D2 keeps TR1 isolated from the scan circuit until time $t_4$ when D3 turns off. Regulation is obtained by the Syclops control circuit comparing the output of the chopper transformer with a reference voltage and adjusting the mark-to-space ratio of the chopper drive pulse waveform accordingly.

## Integrated power supply and line output (IPSALO)

An improvement in the power dissipation of a power supply may be obtained by combining the functions of the chopper and line output transformers into a single transformer known as the **combi-transformer**. The integrated power supply and line output, IPSALO, technique devised by Salora also saves on costs, space and weight of the receiver. Figure 13.20 shows the basic arrangements for an IPSALO circuit in which TR1 is the chopper and TR2 is the line output transistor. The combi-transformer which acts as the mains isolation tranformer provides all d.c. rails including the e.h.t. and the heaters to the tube.

## Self oscillating power supply (SOPS)

The functions of chopper and oscillator may be combined in a single

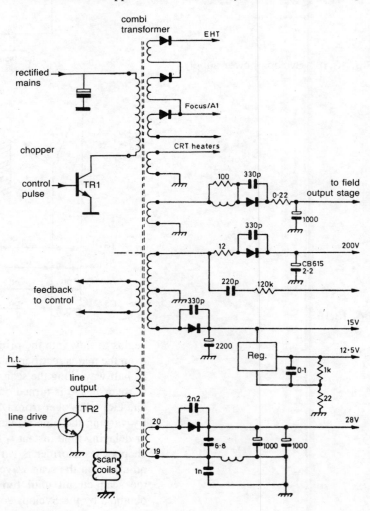

**Fig. 13.20** Integrated power supply and line output, IPSALO

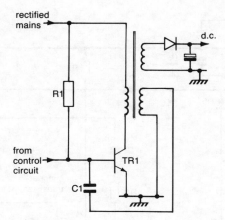

**Fig. 13.21** Block oscillator

transistor to form a self oscillating power supply, SOPS. A secondary winding of the chopper transformer is used to form a blocking oscillator arrangement as shown in Fig. 13.21.

A different arrangement for a blocking oscillator is shown in Fig. 13.22. At switch on, the chopper transistor TR1 begins to conduct as a result of the forward bias applied to its base via start-up resistor R1. Collector current increases which induces a positive voltage across secondary winding S1. This forward biases D1 and further increases TR1 current further. When saturation is reached, the increase in current ceases and a negative voltage is induced across S1 which reverse biases D1 switching TR1 off. At this point, the voltage across primary winding P1 reverses and D2 switches on. The tuned circuit formed by primary winding P1 and C1 begins to oscillate with energy transferring from P1 to C1. For the second half of the cycle, when energy begins to transfer back to P1, diode D2 is reversed biased, oscillations stop and current in P1 reverses causing a positive voltage

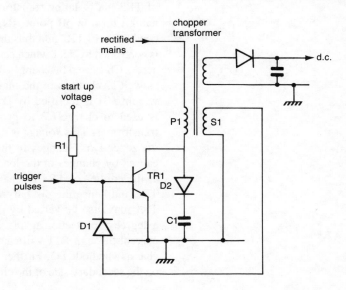

**Fig. 13.22** Different arrangement for a blocking oscillator

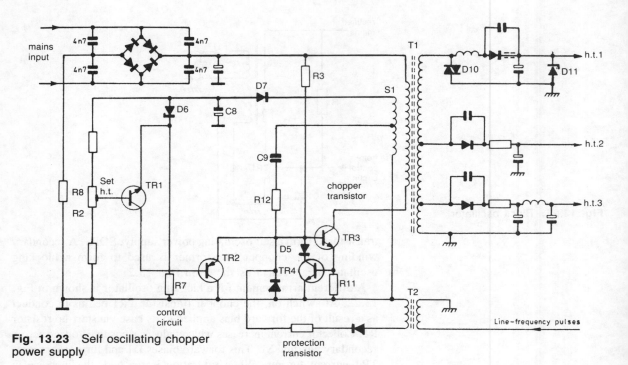

**Fig. 13.23** Self oscillating chopper power supply

to be induced across S1 turning TR1 on and so on. Trigger pulses from the control circuit are used to initiate each cycle to keep the d.c. output constant.

A self oscillating chopper circuit based on a Panasonic chassis is shown in Fig. 13.23 in which TR3 is the chopper/oscillator transistor and C9 is the blocking capacitor which discharges through transistor TR2. Pulses derived from the line output stage are fed to the base of TR3 via isolating transformer T2 to turn TR3 on just before its natural turning off point. Regulation is obtained by controlling the conduction of TR2 and thus the discharge of C9. Transistor TR2 itself is controlled by TR1 which senses any change in the voltage developed across C8 caused by changes in the loading of the chopper transformer as well as changes in the mains input. The voltage across feedback winding S1 is rectified by D7. The negative voltage thus produced is used to charge C8 to provide a measure of the loading of the transformer. This voltage is then used to provide TR1 emitter voltage via zener D6. Changes in the loading of the transformer, whether caused by changes in the loading or in the mains, cause the voltage at the emitter of TR1 to change which determines the base bias of TR2 and hence the discharging current of C9. The current through TR1 may also be varied by the 'set h.t.' control R2. TR4 provides a degree of protection against excessive current taken by TR3. A large current through R11 will cause TR4 to conduct taking TR3 base to chassis via diode D5. Further protection is provided by D10 and D11 on the secondary side of the circuit. T1 and T2 provide mains isolation.

# 14 Television display tubes

It will be recalled that in the c.r.t. the high-speed electrons in the form of a beam current are emitted by an electron gun, focused and accelerated by an electron lens and then directed towards a screen which acts as a positively charged anode. The screen which is coated with phosphor gives a visible glow when hit by high speed electrons. The colour of the emitted light is determined by the type of phosphor used. For monochrome display, only one type of phosphor coating is used. For a colour display, three types of phosphors are used in order to obtain the three primary colours.

## E.h.t.

A final anode voltage known as the extra high tension, e.h.t., in the region of 15–30 kV is required by the tube to attract and accelerate the electrons. This e.h.t. is produced by a voltage multiplier network (Fig. 14.1). The a.c. voltage input is obtained from an overwind on the line output transformer. C1-D1 act as a clamper which charges C1 to the peak of the input voltage, $V_p$. This is then applied to the second clamping circuit consisting of D2-C2 charging C2 to $2V_p$ and so on. The elements of the voltage multiplier are contained in a single well-isolated package or capsule, known as a **tripler**.

## Monochrome tube

The monochrome display tube consists of a single electron gun, an anode assembly acting as the electron lens and a viewing surface. The beam passes through a 4-anode assembly (Fig. 14.2) which provides acceleration (A1), electrostatic focusing (A2/A3) and final e.h.t. anode (A4). As well as the grid potential, the emission of electrons is also dependent upon the potential between the cathode and the first anode. An increase in the potential between these two electrodes causes more electrons to be emitted and vice versa. The actual tube voltages depend on the size of the tube and its design; however, the following are typical voltages for a monochrome receiver tube:

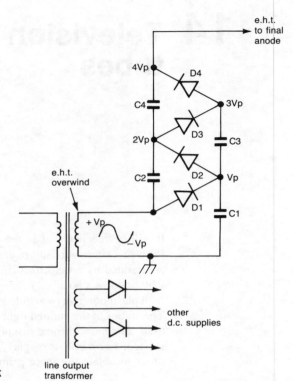

**Fig. 14.1** Voltage multiplier network

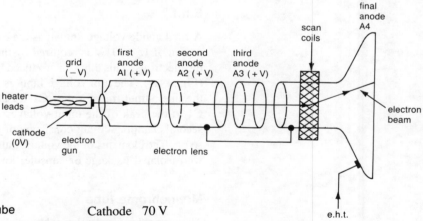

**Fig. 14.2** The cathode ray tube

| | |
|---|---|
| Cathode | 70 V |
| Grid | 30 V |
| A1 | 300–400 V (accelerating anode) |
| A2 | 15–20 kV (connected to final anode) |
| A3 | variable up to 500 V (focus anode) |
| A4 | 15–20 kV (final anode) |

The electron gun and the anode assembly are contained within a vacuumed thick glass envelope as shown in Fig. 14.3. Access to the various electrodes is obtained via pin connections at the back of the neck of the tube with the exception of the final anode which is accessed

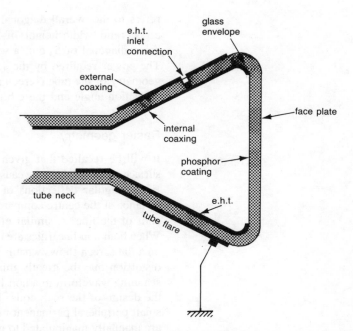

**Fig. 14.3** Display tube glass envelope

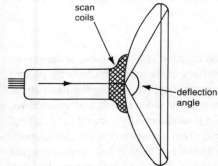

**Fig. 14.4** Beam deflection

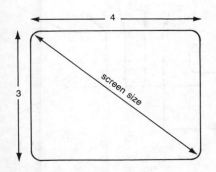

**Fig. 14.5** Screen size

along the tube flare. The inside and outside of the tube flare are coated with a layer of graphite known as **aquadag** coating. The outer coating is connected to chassis and the inner coating is connected to e.h.t. The glass separation between them form a reservoir capacitor for the e.h.t. supply. This is why it is important that this capacitance is fully discharged before handling the tube, otherwise a violent shock may be experienced.

In order to produce a display, the electron beam is deflected in the horizontal (line) and vertical (field) directions. Electromagnetic deflection is employed using two sets of coils (line and field) known as scan coils placed along the neck of the tube as shown in Fig. 14.4. The most common deflection angle is 90° although 100° and 110° are widely used for large screens. The tube's angle of deflection forms an important specification of the c.r.t. It refers to the angle through which the beam is deflected along the diagonal of the screen. The actual angles of deflection in the horizontal and vertical directions are less than the specified value. For instance a typical 110° tube may have a vertical deflection of 81° and a horizontal deflection of 98°. The deflection angle depends on the strength of the magnetic field created by the scan coils, the speed of the electron beam which is a function of the e.h.t. and the thickness of the neck of the tube. A narrow neck allows the scan coils to operate in close proximity to the beam and hence exercise greater influence upon it. Modern receivers have deflection angles of 90° or 110°. Another specification of the c.r.t. is the size of the screen given in centimetres (Fig. 14.5). The quoted figure refers to the diagonal measurement of the visible picture as opposed to the traditional tube size quoted in inches which refers to the overall diagonal measurement of the screen. With an aspect ratio (width:height) of 4:3, a 51 cm (21 inch) tube for instance has a diagonal of 51 cm, a width of 41 cm and a height of 31 cm. The power required by the scan coils is a function of the size and geometry of the tube (screen size and neck diameter) as well as the deflection angle and the e.h.t. applied to the final anode.

## Raster geometry

It will be recalled that given a linear timebase waveform, the flat surface of the display tube causes non-linearity in the displayed picture. Equal angular deflections of the beam cause it to scan a smaller distance at the centre compared with the distance it scans at the two ends of the line. A similar effect is produced for the vertical scan. When both non-linearities are considered together, the raster produced on a flat screen shows what is known as **pincushion distortion**. Such distortion may be greatly minimised by changing the shape of the scanning waveform to a non-linear sawtooth by S-correction and by the design of the scan coils. It can also be corrected by the use of small peripheral permanent magnets placed on the scan coils which are manually manipulated to modify the shape of the magnetic field.

## Beam modulation

In order to produce an image on the tube, the brightness of the screen has to be varied as it scans the surface of the tube to recreate the picture information line by line. This is achieved by varying the intensity of the electron beam in accordance with the video signal, a process known as **beam modulation**. The beam is modulated by varying the potential between the cathode and the grid. There are two types of modulation: **grid modulation** in which the cathode voltage is held constant while the grid voltage is varied by the video signal, and **cathode modulation** in which the voltage at the grid is fixed and that of the cathode is varied with the video signal. With cathode modulation the video signal is negative-going as shown in Fig. 14.6. Peak white is produced when

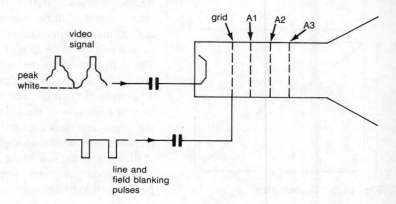

**Fig. 14.6**   Cathode modulation

the cathode is at its most negative potential. Because of its greater sensitivity, cathode modulation is normally used with negative-going blanking pulses being applied to the grid to cut the beam off during line and field flyback.

## Monochrome tube connections

Typical connections to a monochrome tube are shown in Fig. 14.7 with W11 as the rectifier/doubler package providing the 11 kV e.h.t. for the final anode of the tube. Rectifier W13 provides the d.c. supply for the focus anode and the gird. Brightness is controlled by R98 which varies the voltage at the grid. Blanking pulses are applied to the grid via C108/R107 and clipped by diode W15.

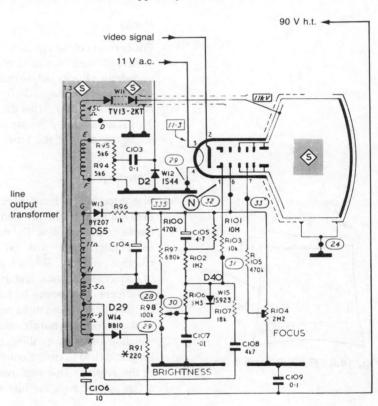

**Fig. 14.7** Monochrome tube connection (Ferguson 1613)

## Colour receiver tubes

It will be recalled that the cathode ray tubes used for colour display have three separate guns, one for each primary colour arranged to bombard a screen which is coated with three different types of phosphors, one for each primary colour. The three phosphors are arranged to form a 3-colour triad. A steel **shadow mask** is placed behind the coated screen which allows the three electron beams to converge and pass through slots before they strike their particular phosphor on the screen. Three primary colours are thus produced which, because they are very close to each other, are added by the human eye to create a sensation of colour.

Colour tubes require higher anode voltages and larger video drives compared with monochrome receivers. Typical voltages are as follows:

| Cathode | 100−150 V |
|---------|-----------|
| Grid | 20−30 V |
| A1 | 500−1000 V |
| Focus | 2−7 kV |
| E.h.t. | 25−30 kV (final anode) |

## Purity

For correct colour reproduction, the red, green and blue beams must strike only their own particular phosphors and no other. This is known as **purity**. Purity adjustment involves changing the strength and direction of the magnetic field created by the scan coils to move the beams so that they strike the correct phosphor coating of the screen. This is achieved by the use of a pair of two-pole ring magnets placed along the neck of the tube.

## Convergence

The three beams form three separate rasters as shown in Fig. 14.8 thus multiplying the problems of raster correction encountered with monochrome displays. The three rasters must not only be of the correct rectangular shape with no pincushion distortion, they must also coincide precisely. This is known as convergence. There are two types of convergence, static and dynamic. **Static convergence** involves the movement of the beams by permanent magnets placed inside or outside the tube to bring the three beams into coincidence in the central area of the screen. **Dynamic convergence** covers the rest of the screen which involves the establishment of a continuously varying (dynamic) magnetic field to ensure convergence at the outlying areas and corners of the display. This requires electromagnetic waveforms which are a function of both the line and field frequencies.

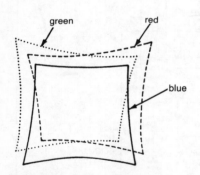

**Fig. 14.8**   R, G, B rasters

## The delta-gun shadow-mask tube

The first mass produced colour tube was the delta-gun. It has three electron guns mounted at 120° to each other at the neck of the tube each with its own electron lens. The guns are tilted by a small amount towards the central axis of the tube so that their electron beams converge and cross at the shadow-mask and pass through carefully positioned holes to strike their correct phosphor dot. A large number of electrons miss their holes and are lost through hitting the mask resulting in what is known as low **electron transparency**, low efficiency and low brightness. The delta arrangement of the three guns makes it difficult to achieve accurate convergence as the beams are made to scan the screen. This is the main disadvantage of the delta tube. Highly complex and expensive convergence circuits are necessary to overcome the two-dimensional distortion of the rasters and to maintain good convergence. Several presets have to be used in a complex sequence requiring highly skilled labour. Furthermore, the tendency for convergence to drift means frequent adjustments are necessary. For this reason, delta-gun tubes are no longer used for domestic TV receivers. However, they are still in production for use as monitors for advanced computer displays because of their high definition when fitted with a very fine-pitch shadow-mask.

### The in-line colour tube

In the in-line shadow-mask tube the three guns are placed side by side and the phosphor coatings on the screen are in the form of striped triads. Each 3-colour triad is arranged to coincide with a longitudinal grill or slot in the shadow mask. Having three beams in the same horizontal plane has two advantages. First, purity is unaffected by horizontal magnetic fields such as the earth's magnetic field. Second, the need for vertical convergence correction disappears because the three beams always travel in the same horizontal plane. Convergence is then reduced to the relatively easy task of deflecting the two outer beams slightly inwards to converge with the central beam. The first in-line tube was developed by Sony and is known as the **trinitron**. This was followed by the Mullard **precision-in-line**, PIL (AX series) self converging tube which eliminated the need for dynamic convergence adjustment altogether.

### The trinitron tube

The trinitron uses a single in-line gun assembly and a single electron lens assembly as shown in Fig. 14.9. The phosphors are arranged in vertical stripes forming three-colour strip triads. The shadow-mask

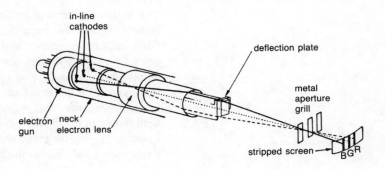

**Fig. 14.9** The trinitron tube

is replaced by a metal aperture grille with one vertical slit for each phosphor triad. Greater electron transparency is achieved as fewer electrons are lost by hitting the mask resulting in improved efficiency and brightness. The single electron gun employs three in-line cathodes. The three beams pass through a complicated anode arrangement which bends the two outer (red and blue) beams so that they seem to be emanating from the same source as the middle green beam. The trinitron suffers from two basic disadvantages. The first is that the striped mask has very little stiffness in the vertical direction and has to be kept under considerable tension to prevent sagging or buckling. The second disadvantage is the need for some dynamic convergence adjustments specially in wide-angle large-screen versions.

### The PIL tube

In the precision-in-line tube, three separate guns are mounted side-by-side on the same horizontal plane. The phosphors are arranged in vertical stripes on the screen and the shadow-mask has the staggered slots shown in Fig. 14.10 which provide mechanical rigidity and high electron transparency resulting in improved brightness. The main advantage of the PIL tube is the development of a special deflection yoke designed to produce a staggered magnetic field known as an **astigmatic field** which eliminates the need for dynamic convergence.

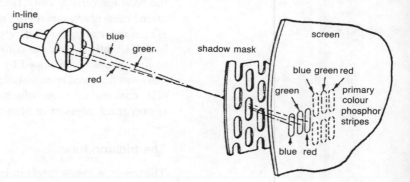

**Fig. 14.10**   The precision-in-line tube

### Self convergence

The angle of deflection applied to an electron beam is proportional to the strength of the magnetic field present along the path of the beam. For a uniform magnetic field, the three beams will be subjected to equal force and will thus converge at the centre of the screen at all points along a circular ring known as the image field (Fig. 14.11a). However, for a flatter screen, the three beams will diverge resulting in misconvergence. This is overcome by the non-uniform or astigmatic field shown in Fig. 14.11b in which the two outer beams move along a path of varying magnetic strength. The centre beam passes through a relatively weak field in the middle of the deflection plane. The two

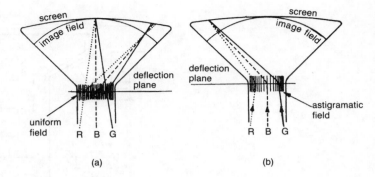

**Fig. 14.11**  Self-converging
astigmatic field

outer beams will suffer different deflections as they move from a
relatively strong field on the outside to a weaker one in the middle.
As a result the deflecting force acting on them is reduced and they
turn through a smaller angle than the centre beam. Provided the
astigmatic field is accurately designed, the three beams will converge
at all points on a line across the flat screen. The same principles apply
to the vertical deflection of the beams resulting in two astigmatic fields
established by the deflection yoke.

Later tube designs such as the Mullard 45AX tube incorporate a
single-gun assembly with a narrow neck. Narrow-neck tubes require
much less deflection energy and their closely spaced beams need less
convergence correction.

## PIL tube connections

Typical connections to a PIL colour tube are shown in Fig. 14.12
in which the e.h.t. tripler capsule also provides the high voltage
required by the focus electrode. Capacitor C730 is charged by the
tripler which is then used to provide the A1 voltage via preset resistor
R721. The return path for the e.h.t. current is via current limiter diode
W722. Diode W722 is forward biased by R724/R725 with a forward
current flowing in the opposite direction to the e.h.t. tube current.
When the tube current exceeds the forward bias current, W722 is cut
off and the tube current is diverted via resistor chain R724/R725. This
causes the voltage at the junction of the two resistors to increase,
increasing the voltage at the grids which reduces the beam current.
The change in voltage is also fed to the luminance amplifier to change
its gain.

## Colour tube adjustments

Even with self-converging tubes, there remain a number of
adjustments that have to be made to produce a fully linear display
with the correct chrominance content. This involves two separate
adjustments: grey-scale and pincushion.

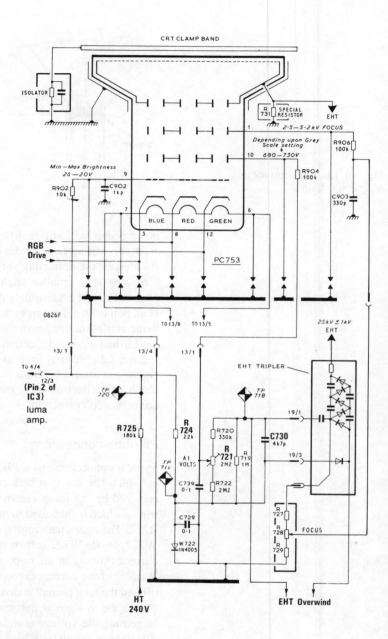

**Fig. 14.12**  PIL tube connections
(Ferguson 9000 chassis)

## Grey-scale tracking

The purpose of grey-scale tracking is to ensure that a monochrome
display exhibits different shades of grey only with no traces of colour
tint at all levels of brightness. Grey scale tracking is carried out on
a staircase or grey-scale display (Fig. 14.13) and involves two types
of adjustments: lowlights (low brightness) and **highlights** (high
brightness). The **lowlights** adjustment brings the cut-off points of the
three guns into coincidence thus ensuring that shaded areas of the

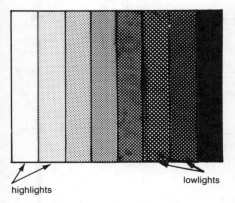

highlights

lowlights

**Fig. 14.13**   Grey scales

picture have no coloured tint. In PIL tubes where the three A1 anodes are connected together, the lowlights adjustment is carried out by varying the d.c. potential of each cathode, a setting that is found at the video output stage. The highlights adjustment ensures that all other white levels are correctly reproduced without a coloured tinting. This is achieved by varying the video signal drive, a setting usually referred to as video gain control.

### Pincushion adjustment

Despite the S-correction described earlier, the screen display still suffers from pincushion distortion specially in wide deflection tubes caused by the flat surface of the screen. It is the result of the joint effect of both the line and field deflection which produces a maximum angle of deflection along the diagonal, hence the stretched corners. Figure 14.14 shows a sketch of a raster with much exaggerated pincushion distortion. The bowing inward of the sides is known as east-west (E-W) distortion and at the top and bottom is referred to as north-south (N-S) distortion. In E-W distortion the scan lines change in length as the beam is deflected vertically, i.e. field by field. E-W distortion is therefore a distortion of a line, the scan line, by the field frequency. Conversely, the N-S distortion is a distortion of the field by line frequency. The correction of both distortions involves modifying the deflection field by the creation of a corrective magnetic field that is equal and opposite to that which created the distortion in the first place.

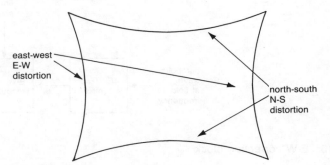

east-west
E-W
distortion

north-south
N-S
distortion

**Fig. 14.14**   Pin-cushioning distortion

Correction along the E-W axis involves reducing the width of the line scan at the top and bottom of the picture until it is the same as that in the middle (Fig. 14.15). This is achieved by modulating the basic line scan sawtooth waveform by a parabolic waveform at the field frequency as shown in Fig. 14.15(c) to produce the necessary correction shown in (b). A block diagram for an E-W correction circuit is shown in Fig. 14.16 in which the modulating parabolic waveform at field frequency may be changed in amplitude and phase by the E-W control. The modulated line waveform is then applied to the line scan coils via transformer coupling T1 to modify the basic current sawtooth scan waveform.

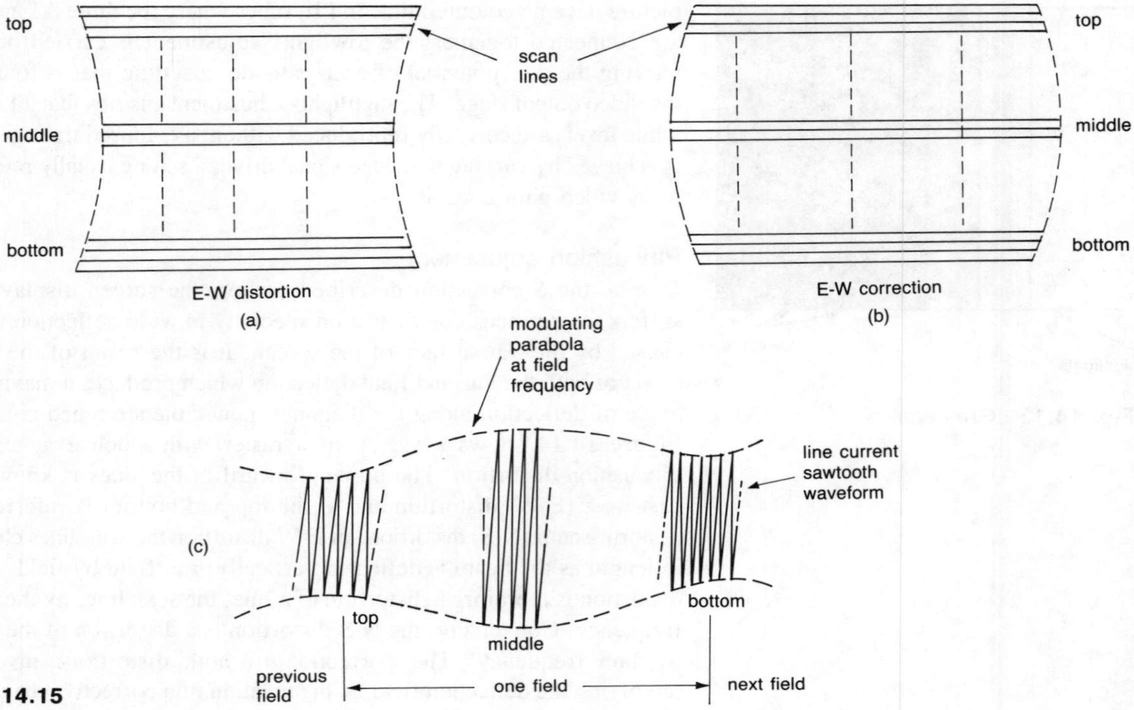

E-W distortion
(a)

E-W correction
(b)

**Fig. 14.15**

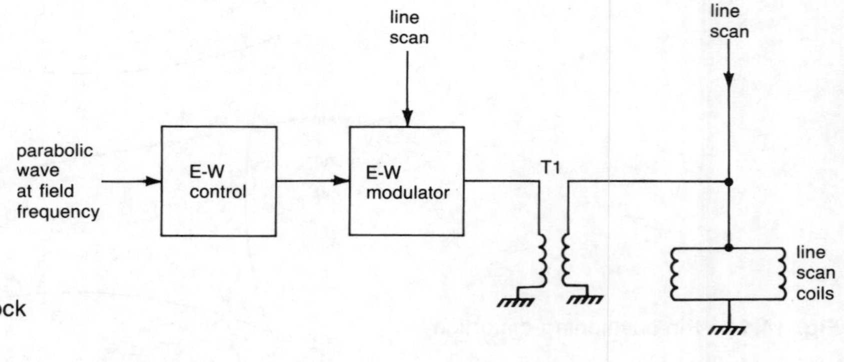

**Fig. 14.16** E-W correction block diagram

Correction along the N-S axis involves modulating the field sawtooth by small parabolic waveforms at line frequency as shown in Fig. 14.17. The amplitude of the parabolas diminishes as the beam reaches the middle of the scan and reverses as it proceeds towards the bottom.

## Degaussing

The magnetic field applied to the three beams may be affected by the earth's magnetic field and any other stray field in the proximity of the receiver including the effect of domestic appliances. The result is impurity in the form of colour patches on the display that cannot

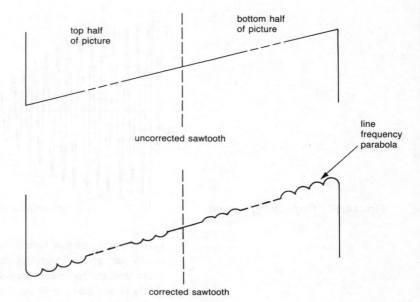

top half
of picture

bottom half
of picture

uncorrected sawtooth

line
frequency
parabola

corrected sawtooth

**Fig. 14.17**  N-W correction

be removed by purity corrections. To avoid these effects, a magnetic shield is fixed over part of the cone of the tube. In addition, the shadow-mask itself together with other steel fittings near the tube face must be demagnetised regularity to avoid impurity and misconvergence. Demagnetisation may be carried out manually by moving a coil known as a degaussing coil slowly in parallel to the face of the screen. The coil, which is energised by an a.c. supply such as the mains, is moved

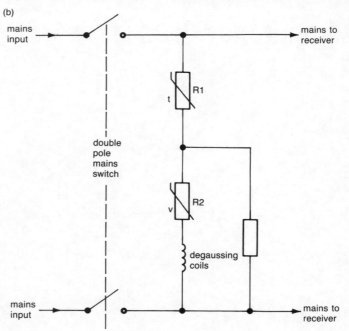

(b)

mains
input

mains to
receiver

R1

t

double
pole
mains
switch

R2

v

degaussing
coils

mains
input

mains to
receiver

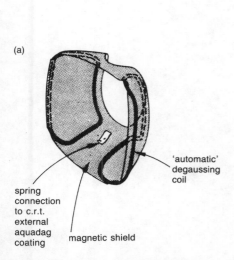

(a)

'automatic'
degaussing
coil

spring
connection
to c.r.t.
external
aquadag
coating

magnetic shield

**Fig. 14.18**   (a) Colour tube magnetic shield, (b) degaussing circuit

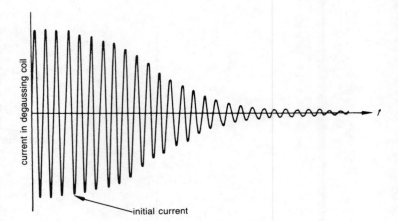

Fig. 14.19  Degaussing current

slowly away, turned face downward and finally turned off when it is few feet away. Everyday degaussing is carried out automatically every time the receiver is switched on. Two degaussing coils are fitted partly inside and partly outside the magnetic shield (Fig. 14.18(a)) and connected to the mains supply as shown in Fig. 14.18(b) in which R1 is a thermistor and R2 is a voltage dependent resistor. Upon switch on, R1 and R2 having very small resistances allows a large a.c. current to flow through the coils which causes the temperature of R1 to rise increasing its resistance. The voltage across R1 also increases and consequently that across R2 falls which increases its own resistance and so on. The combined effect is a decaying current through the coils as shown in Fig. 14.19 which demagnetise the tube.

# 15 Digital processing

Physical matters that act upon our senses such as light or sound are of the analogue type, that is they vary along a continuous curve. For this reason, electronic systems such as audio and TV systems have developed along analogue lines. Advances in digital technology and the manufacture of i.c.s have meant that sound, light and colour values can be expressed and manipulated in digital form, but at either end of the signal chain a transducer must be employed. At the transmitter, the transducer converts the analogue signal into a digital form. At the receiving end, the transducer transforms the digital expressions into an analogue form so they may be interpreted by our senses. The use of digital processing in TV transmission and reception provides a number of advantages and opens new opportunities. At the transmitter it is compatible with digital switching techniques used in TV studios. In the receiver it is compatible with teletex, remote control and NICAM sound transmission. With error detection and correction techniques, digital processing can provide improved transmission quality even in a noisy environment.

With current analogue public broadcasting, digital processing of sections of the receiver may be incorporated in a TV set. Such television sets are known as **analogue/digital receivers**. The major effect of this on the received picture is to produce an extremely steady display which itself produces a subjective improvement in the picture quality. Flickering of the lines and fields may be eliminated with the use of memory devices. The latter may also be used to correct the shape of the raster, reduce the effect of noise and interference on the image on the tube. One of the main advantages of digital processing is realised in the production process. Analogue/digital receivers require less adjustments at the manufacturing stage resulting in reduced labour costs. It is also possible to manufacture multiple standard TV receivers for use in different countries with minimal adjustments.

Digital processing in a TV receiver is amenable to microcomputer control and automatic adjustments such as grey-scale tracking. It opens up wide possibilities such as digital storage, frame freeze and various forms of picture manipulation such as zoom, and multiple displays. Analogue/digital receivers may also be used in conjunction with various other peripheral devices such as computers and printers which may be used to record texts and images.

**Table 15.1**

| Decimel | Binary columns | | |
|---------|------|------|------|
|         | C    | B    | A    |
|         | (4)  | (2)  | (1)  |
| 0 | 0 | 0 | 0 |
| 1 | 0 | 0 | 1 |
| 2 | 0 | 1 | 0 |
| 3 | 0 | 1 | 1 |
| 4 | 1 | 0 | 0 |
| 5 | 1 | 0 | 1 |
| 6 | 1 | 1 | 0 |
| 7 | 1 | 1 | 1 |

**Table 15.2**

| Hexadecimel | Binary |
|-------------|--------|
| 0 | 0000 |
| 1 | 0001 |
| 2 | 0010 |
| 3 | 0011 |
| 4 | 0100 |
| 5 | 0101 |
| 6 | 0110 |
| 7 | 0111 |
| 8 | 1000 |
| 9 | 1001 |
| A | 1010 |
| B | 1011 |
| C | 1100 |
| D | 1101 |
| E | 1110 |
| F | 1111 |

## Digital transmission

Unlike analogue signals which are continuous and may take an infinite number of instantaneous values, a digital signal uses the binary system with two discrete levels: a logic '0' known as space and represented by 0 V and a logic '1' known as mark and represented by a certain voltage, normally 5 V. A single binary digit, known as a **bit**, provides basic 'YES' or 'NO' information. More information may be conveyed by grouping a number of bits together, e.g. 4, 8, 16. Such groupings are known as **words**. A word is a group of binary digits or bits which form the basic unit of information in a digital system. A four-bit word known as a **nibble** can be used to represent $2^4 = 16$ different numbers from 0 to 15. An eight-bit word known as a **byte** can represent $2^8 = 256$ different numbers from 0 to 255 and so on.

In the same way as denary (decimal) columns represent increasing powers of 10, binary columns represent increasing powers of 2 with the rightmost bit known as the least significant bit (LSB) having a value of $2^0 = 1$. The next column has a value of $2^1 = 2$, the third $2^2 = 4$ and so on, as shown in Table 15.1. In any binary word, the leftmost bit is known as the most significant bit, MSB.

## Hexadecimal

In order to avoid the use of long strings of binary digits, hexadecimal notation is used. Hexadecimal numbers have a base of 16 and hence have 16 distinct symbols:

$$0, 1, 2, 3, 4, 5, 6, 7, 8, 9, A, B, C, D, E, F$$

with A, B, C, D, E and F representing denary numbers 10, 11, 12, 13, 14 and 15 respectively. Each 4-bit binary number may thus be represented by a single hexadecimal digit as shown in Table 15.2. An 8-bit binary number is represented by a 2-digit hexadecimal number and a 12-bit binary by a 3-digit hexadecimal number as shown in Fig. 15.1. To avoid confusion, the base (2 for binary and 16 for hexadecimal) may be shown as a subscript, e.g. $1001_2$ and $A3_{16}$. A more common way of distinguishing between the two types of numbering systems is to terminate binary numbers with a 'B' and

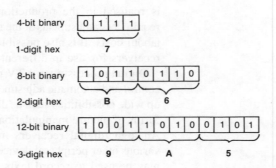

**Fig. 15.1**

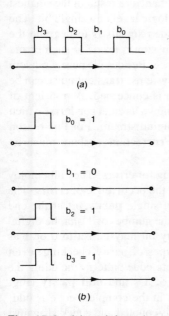

**Fig. 15.2** (a) serial mode,
(b) parallel mode

hexadecimal numbers with a 'H'. For instance, binary 0110 is written as 0110B and hexadecimal number 2F as 2FH.

## Serial and parallel transmission

Digital transmission is the process of sending data in the form of a series of pulses down a line or by radio wave from one place to another, a process known as pulse code modulation, PCM. Digital data may be transmitted in one of two modes: the serial and the parallel (Fig. 15.2). In the serial mode the bits are transferred in sequence, one after the other: $b_0$, $b_1$, $b_2$ and so on. In the parallel mode, the bits are transferred simultaneously along a number of parallel lines, one line for each bit, in synchronism. While parallel transmission is fast since complete words are sent at each clock pulse, it requires as many lines as there are bits in the word. For this reason, serial mode is used for transmission over medium and long distances. Another important consideration is the number of pins that must be made available on an i.c. to accommodate parallel data transmission. For large multi-bit systems the number of pins may be so large as to make construction impractical.

Digital transmission is synchronised by the system clock which also determines the speed of transmission known as the **bit rate**. For instance a 6-bit word transmitted serially on a single line has a bit rate given by

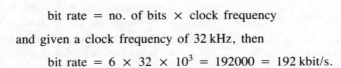

and given a clock frequency of 32 kHz, then

$$\text{bit rate} = 6 \times 32 \times 10^3 = 192000 = 192\,\text{kbit/s}.$$

In the serial mode, a start and stop bit are normally added at either end of the word.

## Multiplexing

One method that is commonly used to reduce the number of lines and therefore the number of pins on the chip is multiplexing. Two or more sets of data are made to share a single set of lines on a **time-sharing** basis with each set of data occupying the lines for part of the time. The sets of data sharing the parallel lines may form part of a complete word. For instance, an 8-bit word may be transmitted along four lines by multiplexing one half of the word, the most significant four bits, with the other half, the least significant four bits. At the receiving end, a demultiplexer is used to reconstruct the complete word. Multiplexing may also be used in the serial mode of transmission in which different channels may be made to share a single line on a time-sharing basis as is the practice in telephony and other data transmission systems.

## Error detection

Unlike analogue transmission in which small errors in the received signal may not affect the operation of the system in a significant way, a data communication may suffer a fatal fault as a result of the smallest possible error, namely a change of the logic level of a single bit. The effect of errors on digital sound or video signals is to degrade the quality of reproduction. Digital transmission is prone to such errors which are caused by noise and interference. Besides the purely random noise encountered on communication systems, transient noise can be devastating as far as data transmission is concerned. A transient of say 10 ms duration can cause what is known as an **error burst** which may obliterate a number of bits in a digital stream. For this reason some form of error detection and correction system must be incorporated.

There are several methods of checking for errors. They all employ additional (or redundant) bits to detect the occurrence of errors. The simplest technique is the addition of a single **parity bit** at the end of the digital code to indicate whether the number of 1's in the digital coded word is even or odd. The parity bit may be set to 0 or 1 as shown in Fig. 15.3. There are two types of parity checking: **even parity** (Fig. 15.3(a)) when the complete code pattern (including the parity bit) contains an even number of 1's and **odd parity** (Fig. 15.3(b)) when the total number of 1's in the complete code is odd. At the receiving end the number of 1's is counted and checked against the parity bit. A difference indicates an error. The basic drawback of the simple parity check is that it can only detect a single bit error. An error affecting two bits will go undetected. Furthermore, there is no provision for determining which bit is actually in error. For these reasons a more sophisticated system of error detection is normally used.

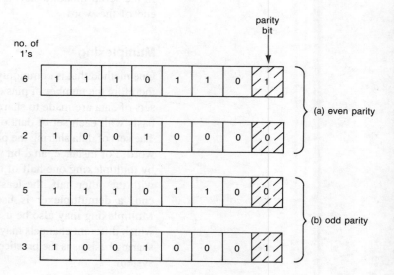

Fig. 15.3

One method for detecting the actual wrong bits is based on the generation of a **parity word** for a group of digital codes arranged in a block of columns and rows. A parity bit for each row and column is generated to form a parity word. At the receiving end, the parity of each column and row is checked and if an error is indicated, the precise bit may be identified.

An alternative method is the use of **interleaving** in which a block of digital codes including their parity bits are arranged in a matrix consisting of a number of columns and rows. The bits within the block are then transmitted column by column. Interleaving is a simple and powerful error detection technique which is capable of detecting a number of simultaneous bits that may be in error. Interleaving may also be used to minimise the effect of error burst by separating adjacent bits, a technique employed very successfully in NICAM digital transmission.

## Digital coding

The conversion of a quantity or a number into a digital format may be carried out using one of a number of codes. The natural binary code is that listed in Table 15.1 in which the columns of say a 4-bit binary number represent progressively increasing powers of 2 giving a count of 0 to 15. Such a count is not very appropriate for denary applications. A more appropriate coding system is the **binary-coded** decimal, BCD, which converts each denary digit into a four-bit binary number. A two-digit denary number will thus result in two groups of four-bit binary numbers (eight bits in total) as shown in Table 15.3. Another popular coding technique is the Gray code which ensures that only one bit changes state as the denary number is progressively incremented as shown in Table 15.4. The Gray code avoids the problems of spurious transitional codes associated with the BCD technique.

## Twos complement

The coding techniques considered so far provide positive quantities of unsigned numbers. For instance an eight-bit binary may have values between

0000 0000 binary = 00 denary, and
1111 1111 binary = 255 denary

all of which are positive. In order to distinguish a negative number from a positive one, a − sign is used to precede a denary number e.g. −25. In the binary system, the negative sign itself is given a binary code so that it may be recognised by a digital system. A binary bit known as the **sign bit** is introduced to the left of the MSB of the binary number which is devoted entirely to indicate the sign of the number. Such numbers are often referred to as **sign-and-magnitude**.

**Table 15.3**

| Denary number | BCD |
|---|---|
| 00 | 0000 0000 |
| 01 | 0000 0001 |
| 02 | 0000 0010 |
| 03 | 0000 0011 |
| 04 | 0000 0100 |
| 05 | 0000 0101 |
| 06 | 0000 0110 |
| 07 | 0000 0111 |
| 08 | 0000 1000 |
| 09 | 0000 1001 |
| 10 | 0001 0000 |
| 11 | 0001 0001 |
| ............ | ............ |
| 57 | 0101 0111 |
| ............ | ............ |
| 83 | 1000 0011 |
| ............ | ............ |
| 99 | 1001 1001 |

**Table 15.4**

| Denary | Binary code | Gray code |
|---|---|---|
| 0 | 0000 | 0000 |
| 1 | 0001 | 0001 |
| 2 | 0010 | 0011 |
| 3 | 0011 | 0010 |
| 4 | 0100 | 0110 |
| 5 | 0101 | 0111 |
| 6 | 0110 | 0101 |
| 7 | 0111 | 0100 |
| 8 | 1000 | 1100 |
| 9 | 1001 | 1101 |
| 10 | 1010 | 1111 |
| 11 | 1011 | 1110 |
| 12 | 1100 | 1010 |
| 13 | 1101 | 1011 |
| 14 | 1110 | 1001 |
| 15 | 1111 | 1000 |

When the sign bit is set to 0, the number is positive and when it is set to 1 the number is negative. It follows that a signed eight-bit number has its magnitude indicated by the first seven bits, 0–6, while its sign is indicated by bit 7. An eight-bit code will thus have a range of

[1] 111 1111 = − 127, and
[0] 111 1111 = + 127

where the bit in brackets is the sign bit.

The sign-and-magnitude system of representation is not conducive to arithmetic operations using positive and negative numbers. To overcome this limitation, the twos complement representation of negative numbers is used which automatically produces the correct sign following arithmetic operations.

For positive binary numbers, the twos complement is identical to the sign-and-magnitude system in that it also uses the MSB as the sign bit leaving the remaining bits to indicate the magnitude.

For negative numbers the twos complement is obtained by first producing the complement of the original binary number (with a positive sign) and then adding a 1 to the least significant bit (LSB). The complement of binary 1 is 0 and that of binary 0 is 1. Hence the complement of a binary number is obtained by inverting all its digits, i.e. changing all 1's to 0's and all 0's to 1's.

For example, the twos complement for +54 is given as

$$+54 = [0]\ 0110110$$

However, to find the twos compliment for − 54, start with its positive equivalent:

|  |  | sign bit |
|---|---|---|
| + 54 | = | 0 0110110 |
| compliment | = | 1 1001001 |
|  |  | + 1 |
| twos compliment | = | 1 1001010 |

Table 15.5 shows the conversion of denary numbers into eight-bit twos complement codes.

## Digital memory chips

A memory chip consists of a number of memory cells into which data bits may be stored (or written). The stored data may then be retrieved (or read) from the device. These memory cells are grouped together to form a memory location (e.g. a one-bit, two-bit, four-bit or eight-bit memory location). Each location is given a unique binary code known as an address for the purposes of identification.

Consider Fig. 15.4 which represents the arrangement for eight 4-bit memory locations. Each location has four memory cells; D0, D1,

**Table 15.5**

| Denary no. | twos complement |
|---|---|
| + 127 | 0 111 1111 |
| + 126 | 0 111 1110 |
| + 2 | 0 000 0010 |
| + 1 | 0 000 0001 |
| Zero | 0 000 0000 |
| − 1 | 1 111 1111 |
| − 2 | 1 111 1110 |
| − 126 | 1 000 0010 |
| − 127 | 1 000 0001 |
| − 128 | 1 000 0000 |

Binary address    Memory cells
$A_2$  $A_1$  $A_0$    $D_3$  $D_2$  $D_1$  $D_0$

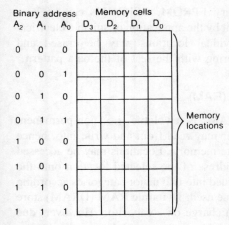

**Fig. 15.4**   Eight 4-bit memory

D2 and D3 into which a four-bit word may be stored. Each location is identified by a unique three-digit (A0, A1, A2) binary **address**; 000, 001, 010 ... 110, 111. A three-digit binary number can address up to $2^3 = 8$ locations. In order to be able to address a bigger memory store with a larger number of locations, a binary address of a higher order must be used. For example, to address 16 ($= 2^4$) different locations, four digits (A0, A1, A2, A3) are necessary and to address 32 locations five digits are required and so on. A memory store with $2^{10} = 1024$ locations is known as having a 1k memory. Such a memory device requires a 10-digit address: A0, A1, ..., A9. The actual size of the memory is determined by the number of bits in each location as well as the number of locations available on the device. Hence a memory chip with 1024 locations with each location consisting of two memory cells or bits has a total memory capacity of 1k $\times$ 2 = 1024 $\times$ 2 = 2048 bits in total.

## Read Only Memory (ROM)

Read only memory (ROM) is a non-volatile memory used for storing data permanently. The data stored can only be read by the user, hence its name, and no new data can be written into the device. ROM is programmed by the manufacturer in accordance with the user specifications.

## Programmable Read Only Memory (PROM)

The fact that ROMs are programmed by the manufacturer means that they can be expensive unless they are produced in large quantities. Furthermore, subsequent changes to the programme once it has been written into ROM are very costly. To avoid this, programmable read only memory chips are used. PROMs fulfil the same basic function as a ROM except that they may be programmed by the user and not by the manufacturer. Once programmed, the data stored in a PROM cannot be altered.

## Erasable programmable read only memory (EPROM)

The main disadvantage of PROM devices is the fact they cannot be reprogrammed. Mistakes in programming thus cannot be corrected. The EPROM overcomes this by allowing the user to delete or erase the stored data and thus change the programme. The stored programme in an EPROM may be erased by exposing the memory cells to ultra-violet light through a 'window' on the i.c. package.

## Electrically erasable programmable read only memory (EEPROM)

Electrically erasable programmable read only memory overcomes the disadvantages of the ordinary EPROM. EEPROMs can be programmed and erased in circuit by the application of suitable electrical signals. Furthermore, individual locations may be erased and programmed without interfering with the rest of the data pattern.

### Random access memory (RAM)

Random access memory, RAM, is a volatile, i.e. non-permanent memory chip, which the user may read from and write into, hence it is also known as read/write memory. Locations may be accessed at random by placing the address of the selected location onto the address lines. RAMs are divided into two major categories according to the type of storage technique used. **Dynamic RAM** (DRAM) store information in the form of a charge on a capacitor. However, due to leakage, the charge is lost and has to be restored; a process known as 'refreshing' the cell. Dynamic RAMs have the advantage of higher density and lower power consumption. **Static** read only memory devices employ flip-flops as the basic cell and hence require no refreshing. Static RAMs will hold data as long as d.c. power is applied to the device.

### Digital processing in a TV receiver

Figure 15.5 shows the principles of digital processing in a TV set receiving analogue broadcast signals. The u.h.f. analogue signal is received in the normal way by the aerial. Following i.f. amplification and detection by the video demodulator, the composite video is fed to the analogue-to-digital converter, ADC. The ADC acts as a pulse-code modulator (PCM) encoder translating the analogue input into a coded multi-line digital stream of pulses. Binary coded decimal, Gray code or other coding techniques may be used. The digitised composite video is then fed to the digital processing unit. A number of chips are used to perform a variety of functions including chrominance decoding, matrixing, clamping, blanking, horizontal and vertical deflection and other controls such as contrast and brightness. Luminance and chrominance delay is implemented in a RAM chip.

**Fig. 15.5**  Principle of digital processing

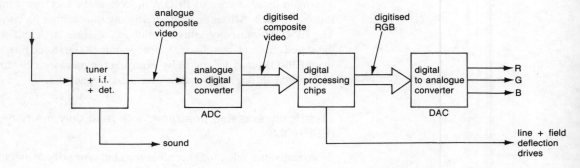

Data bits of digitised signals are written into successive memory cells of a RAM chip. The chip is then put in the read mode and the bits are retrieved resulting in time delay. The amount of delay is determined by the number of memory cells used for each bit of data.

The digitised RGB signals from the digital processor are then fed into a digital-to-analogue converter (DAC) to translate the digitised primary colour signals back into an analogue form before going into the c.r.t. via appropriate output stages. The digital-to-analogue and analogue-to-digital converters may be incorporated into a single i.c. known as **code-decode** or **codec** chip. Furthermore, the digital processor carries out the necessary sync. separation and timebase generation to produce the required drives for the line and field output stages. Sound may also be digitally processed using NICAM technique as will be explained later.

Digital processing may take place after the separation of the composite video into its separate individual components: luminance, Y and the two colour difference signals, $B' - Y'$ and $R' - Y''$. The three separate components are then digitised by an analogue-to-digital converter before going into the digital processor. This technique is known as component coding as opposed to the composite coding shown in Fig. 15.5. Composite coding will be used for the rest of this chapter as this is the most popular technique employed by TV manufacturers.

### The analogue-to-digital converter (ADC)

The analogue-to-digital converter (ADC) is a pulse-code modulator. It takes the analogue input, samples it and then converts the amplitude of each sample to a digital code as shown in Fig. 15.6. The output is a number of parallel digital bits (four in Fig. 15.6) whose simultaneous logic states represent the amplitude of each sample in turn. A variety of codes may be used for such representation including the natural binary code.

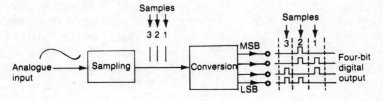

**Fig. 15.6** Analogue-to-digital conversion

### Sampling

The Shannon theory of sampling states that for satisfactory results the analogue signal must be sampled at a rate which is at least twice the highest frequency of the baseband of the original analogue input. This sampling rate is known as the **Nyquist rate**. When the samples are reproduced and the dots are joined together, the reconstructed waveform contains all the information of the original analogue

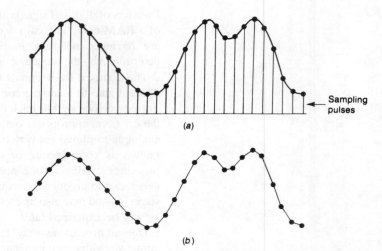

**Fig. 15.7** Reconstruction of a sampled waveform

waveform. Figure 15.7 shows the sampling and reconstruction of an analogue waveform. If the sampling rate was lower than the Nyquist rate, i.e. comparable to the highest frequency of the analogue signal, an overlap would occur between the sidebands produced by the sampling pulses. This causes an effect known as aliasing to occur which makes it impossible to recover the original signal without distortion.

As far as digital processing in a TV receiver is concerned, the highest composite signal frequency is 5.5 MHz. Theoretically, therefore, a sampling frequency of $2 \times 5.5 = 11$ MHz will be adequate. However, in practice a whole multiple of the colour subcarrier frequency is used to avoid inter-modulation between the sampling clock pulse and the subcarrier frequency caused by the non-linearity of the analogue-to-digital conversion process. Sampling at a whole multiple of the subcarrier frequency has a number of other operational advantages including a simplified composite processing and a more convenient conversion process in the case of component coding. The lowest multiple that gives a sampling frequency greater than the Nyquist rate is three times the subcarrier frequency, i.e. $3 \times 4.434 = 13.3$ MHz. Sampling at four times the subcarrier frequency, $4 \times 4.434 = 17.7$ MHz is more commonly used resulting in further operational benefits in terms of a simplified colour decoding technique.

### Quantising

The final stage of the ADC is the conversion process itself. A number of levels, e.g. 0.25, 0.5, 0.75, 1.0 and so on, are established with each level given a binary code. This is known as **quantising**. The number of these 'quantum' steps or discrete levels is determined by the number of bits at the converter output. For instance in a three-bit ADC, the binary output can have a coded value from 000 to 111,

**Table 15.6**

| Level sample | Voltage (V) | Binary code MSB | | LSB |
|---|---|---|---|---|
| 0 | 0 | 0 | 0 | 0 |
| 1 | 0.25 | 0 | 0 | 1 |
| 2 | 0.50 | 0 | 1 | 0 |
| 3 | 0.75 | 0 | 1 | 1 |
| 4 | 1.00 | 1 | 0 | 0 |
| 5 | 1.25 | 1 | 0 | 1 |
| 6 | 1.50 | 1 | 1 | 0 |
| 7 | 1.75 | 1 | 1 | 1 |

a total of eight levels. Now suppose that a scale or a 'quantum' of 250 mV is used, then Table 15.6 listing sample voltages and their corresponding binary codes will apply.

## Quantising noise

With the input being analogue (i.e. continuous), sample voltages will invariably fall between the quantum levels. Hence there is always an element of uncertainty or ambiguity in terms of the value of the least significant bit, LSB. This uncertainty gives rise to a quantising (or ± 1) error, an error that is inherent in any digital coding of analogue values. The quantising error gives rise to quantising distortion, known as quantising noise. The effect of noise is that some of the binary digits are received incorrectly which distort the reconstructed waveform.

Quantising noise has a constant quantity equal to 1/2 the quantum level. The effect of quantising noise therefore is more noticeable at low analogue signal voltages resulting in a poor signal-to-noise (S/N) ratio. For instance, using Table 15.6, with a quantum level of 250 mV, a binary code of 110 may represent a voltage from 1.375 V to 1.625 V, i.e.

$$\text{quantised level} = 1.500 \text{ V} \pm 1/2 \text{ quantum}$$
$$= 1.500 \text{ V} \pm 1/2 \times 0.250 \text{ V}$$
$$= 1.500 \pm 0.125 \text{ V}.$$

This gives a signal-to-noise ratio of

$$\text{S/N} = 1.5/0.125 = 12 \text{ or } 21.6 \text{ dB } (20 \log 12).$$

For a smaller analogue signal level, e.g. 0.25 V, the signal-to-noise ratio is

$$\text{S/N} = 0.25/0.125 = 2 \text{ or } 6 \text{ dB } (20 \log 2).$$

## Companding

While the quantising error cannot be wholly avoided, it can be minimised by improving the resolution of the converter through increasing the number of bits used and thus reducing the quantum level, the quantising error and the quantising noise. However, this still leaves weak signals with a poor signal-to-noise ratio. To overcome this, non-linear quantising may be used in which the quantum level for weak signals is decreased and that for strong signals increased. At the receiving end a complementary non-linear digital-to-analogue conversion is employed to reproduce the original analogue signal. This non-linear coding/decoding technique, called companding, tends to equalise the signal-to-noise ratio over the range of sample amplitudes generated by the analogue signal. Another companding technique which accomplishes the same result is to use an analogue voltage compressor to precede a linear encoder. The companded analogue voltage from the voltage compressor gives prominence to weaker signal levels. After the decoding stage, a complementary expander is used to restore the original signal. Companding may also be used to reduce the number of output bits for the same number of quantum levels, a highly desirable outcome with limited bandwidths.

## Video encoding

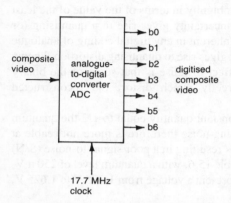

**Fig. 15.8** Seven-bit analogue-to-digital converter

Digital processing of video signals requires a digital code with a minimum of six bits giving $2^6 = 64$ different levels. Assuming a peak-to-peak input voltage of 1 V, a quantum step of 1 V/63 = 16 mV is obtained. A six-bit code will enable an acceptable picture to be reproduced. In practice, however, seven- or eight-bit codes are used for a better quality picture. Figure 15.8 shows a seven-bit analogue-to-digital converter driven by a 17.7 MHz sampling clock.

For a digital broadcast system a minimum of 256 quantum levels, i.e. an eight-bit code, are necessary. To that must be added the redundant bits for error detection. For our purposes, the coding and decoding are carried out within the receiver with little possibility of the noise and the interference associated with TV broadcasting. Hence there is no need for error detection rendering the system far simpler than those required if the broadcast system itself was digitally coded.

## Flash ADC

There are many types of analogue-to-digital converters on the market. For TV processing application a fast and accurate ADC such as the flash (also known as simultaneous) converter is necessary. A typical arrangement for a six-bit flash type ADC chip is shown in Fig. 15.9.

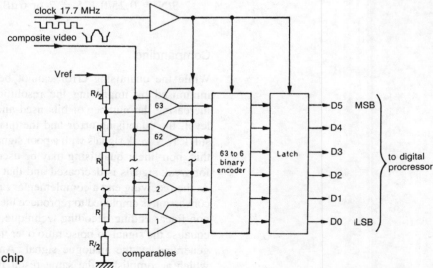

**Fig. 15.9** Six-bit flash ADC chip

It consists of 63 comparators, one for each quantum step above zero. One input of each comparator is connected to a tapping point along a potential divider chain consisting of 64 separate resistors connected to a reference voltage, $V_{ref}$. Each resistor provides one quantum step. The resistor chain thus provides each comparator with a constant reference voltage that is progressively increasing in steps of one quantum. The value of the quantum step is determined by the reference voltage. For instance given a reference voltage of 0.96 V, then the quantum step is given by

$$\text{quantum step} = V_{ref}/64 = 0.96/64 = 15\,\text{mV}.$$

The composite video input is simultaneously applied to the second sampling inputs of each comparator. Comparisons thus take place between the instantaneous value of the input signal and 63 different voltage levels. When the instantaneous value of the input is higher than the portion of the reference voltage fed into the particular comparator, the comparator conducts and a logic 1 is obtained at its output. Thus an input level equal to two quanta results in the bottom two comparators conducting, and an input of three quanta results in the bottom three comparators conducting and so on. The input level is therefore quantised into 64 steps. At each positive (or negative) edge of the 17.7 MHz sampling clock, the comparators are enabled, feeding one quantised sample into the binary encoder which converts the 63-line quantised output from the comparators into a six-bit binary code. At the second clock edge, a second sample is encoded and so on. The output from the 63-to-6 binary encoder is latched to hold the six-bit code long enough for the digital processor to accurately capture the information. The latch is cleared regularly by the sampling clock ready to store the next coded sample and so on.

## Digital-to-analogue converter (DAC)

The digital-to-analogue converter receives a parallel digital input and converts it back to a voltage (or a current) value that is represented by the binary input. If this is repeated for successive coded inputs, an analogue waveform may be reconstructed. For instance, assuming a three-bit binary input, then 000 will be represented by a zero output and 111 by a maximum voltage output determined by the reference voltage $V_{ref}$ in Fig. 15.10. Other inputs are reproduced as a

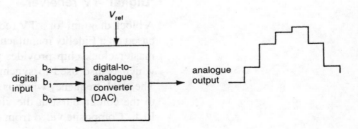

**Fig. 15.10**

proportion of $V_{ref}$, e.g. 001 as 1/8 $V_{ref}$, 011 as 3/8 $V_{ref}$ and 110 as 6/8 (or 3/4) $V_{ref}$. Each bit of the binary input is reproduced in accordance with its weighting giving the following general formula:

$$\text{Output level} = V_{ref} (B2/2 + B1/4 + B0/8)$$

A typical block diagram for a DAC chip is shown in Fig. 15.11. The eight-bit input data is fed into a temporary store via a buffering stage. The store is in the form of an eight-bit register which samples the input data at regular intervals determined by the clock frequency. It holds each eight-bit coded data long enough for the switching/resistor converter network to capture and decode the input. At each clock pulse, the register updates its contents with the next incoming eight-bit code and so on.

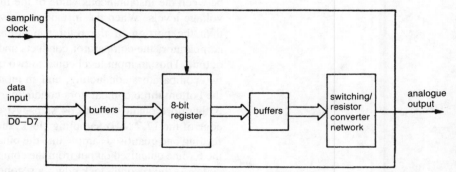

**Fig. 15.11** Digital-to-analogue chip configuration

The switching/resistor converter network is normally of the R-2R ladder type which converts the succession of eight-bit coded data into an analogue waveform. A common arrangement for a R-2R ladder converter is shown in Fig. 15.12 which contains eight electronic switches, one for each bit. The position of the switches is determined by the logic state of the relevant bit. When all the bits are 0, all the switches are down connected to chassis and the output is zero. When one bit has a logic 1, the relevant switch is connected to the reference voltage line $V_{ref}$. A portion of the reference voltage then appears at the output depending on the weighting of the bit. For instance if the most significant bit (MSB) had a logic 1 and the other bits were at logic 0, then an output of 1/2 $V_{ref}$ will be produced representing the correct weighting of most significant bit and so on.

## 'Digital' TV receiver

A block diagram for a TV receiver employing digital video processing based on a Fidelity manufactured chassis is shown in Fig. 15.13. The master clock chip provides a 17.7 MHz sampling pulse waveform which is also used to synchronise the operation of the other units. The clock frequency which is four times the colour subcarrier is locked to the colour burst at the video processor by a phase-locked loop, PLL. Composite video from the vision detector is fed to an analogue-to-digital converter which usually forms one half of a coder/decoder,

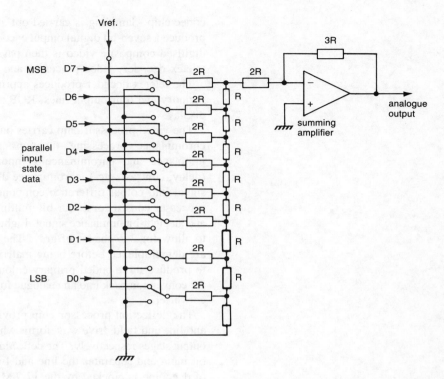

**Fig. 15.12**   R-2R ladder DAC

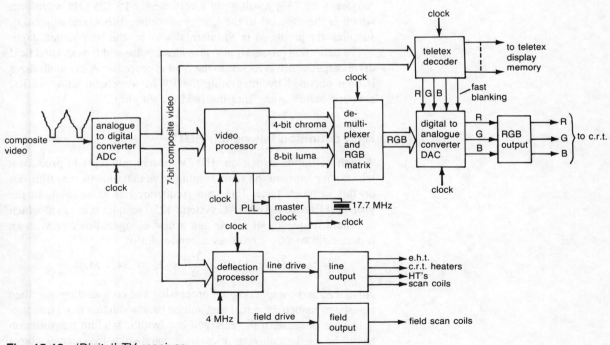

**Fig. 15.13**   'Digital' TV receiver

codec chip. Sampling is carried out at a frequency of 17.7 MHz to produce a seven-bit digital output encoded in BCD or Gray code. The digitised composite video is then passed via a seven-bit bus to the teletex decoder, video processor and deflection processor chips.

The teletex decoder produces appropriate outputs for the display memory and four output lines, RGB and fast blanking for the c.r.t. display.

The video processor chip carries out all necessary luminance and chrominance processing functions including the separation of luminance and chrominance components, luminance processing (delay, contrast, etc.), chrominance delay and decoding of the PAL signal into colour difference components. The output of the video processor consists of a four-bit multiplexed colour difference signal and an eight-bit luminance signal. Eight bits are used for the luminance to allow for 256 shades of grey. The two colour difference signals are demultiplexed before being matrixed with the luminance signal to produce three coded primary colour signals, R, G and B, ready for conversion back into an analogue format by the digital-to-analogue converter.

The deflection processor chip provides timebase synchronisation and line and field drive waveforms which feed into the line and field output stages respectively. The deflection processor decodes the seven-bit input and separates the line and field sync. pulses. The process of decoding is clocked by the 17.7 MHz pulse. The processor also receives a 4 MHz reference frequency from a central control unit, CCU (not shown). The line frequency is obtained by dividing this frequency by 256, resulting in a very steady 15.625 kHz waveform which is then locked to the line sync. pulse. E.h.t. and other d.c. supplies are produced in the normal way by the line output stage.

The deflection processor also provides a pulse-width modulated field drive output which is locked to the field sync. pulse. A sawtooth drive is then obtained by integrating the PWM waveform using an RC network before going into the field output chip.

## High definition television, HDTV

A high definition television, HDTV system, attempts to produce a television picture to the same resolution as that of a 16 mm film. To do this, a much faster line scan frequency has to be used. In the proposed European HDMAC system, 1250 scan lines are used which at a field frequency of 50 Hz and a new elongated picture with an aspect ratio of 16 : 9 requires a bandwidth of

$$\frac{1}{2} \times 1250 \times 1250 \times \frac{16}{9} \times 25 = 34.7 \text{ MHz.}$$

Advanced and complex digital processing and companding may then be used to reduce the actual transmitted bandwidth to a more manageable size. Because of the enlarged bandwidth, satellite transmission has to be used employing microwave bandwidth frequencies above 1 GHz.

# 16 NICAM digital stereo sound

The system of transmitting sound used in British 625-line TV broadcasting employs a sound frequency modulated carrier placed just outside the video spectrum. It can be used to provide a good quality sound given good quality sound amplification at the receiver. However, it is incapable of producing hi fi quality and unable to carry stereophonic sound. Stereo sound has been successfully transmitted by v.h.f. radio broadcasting using analogue modulation of a f.m. carrier. Such a system does not readily commend itself for TV broadcasting because of its bandwidth requirements. It is not possible to add a second sound carrier between 6 and 8 MHz to the video frequency spectrum without causing unacceptable interference to either the vision or the primary 6 MHz sound carrier. To avoid this, compromises will have to be reached which would defeat the original aim of stereo hi fi sound transmission.

After years of research and development BBC engineers came out with a radically new sound system for TV broadcasting using state of the art technology. The system became known as NICAM 728 or NICAM for short. NICAM stands for near instantaneous companded audio multiplex and 728 refers to the data rate of 728 kbit/s. It provides two completely independent sound channels so that dual-language sound tracks may be transmitted as well as stereophonic sound. It can carry data in one or both channels and is completely separate and independent of the existing f.m. monophonic sound channel.

The NICAM system is a classic example of how a digitised waveform can have its coded data manipulated in a variety of ways (scattered, compressed, companded, interleaved and scrambled) and yet can be reconstituted without any loss of the original information. It heavily relies on modern digital technology and on the ability of i.c. manufacturers to make very complex digital chips at low cost. NICAM has been accepted by the UK government as the standard for stereo broadcasting and is recommended by the European Broadcasting Union as the digital standard for terrestrial i.e. land stereo broadcasting in Europe. It is now being considered as a possible international standard by the International Standards Radio Consultative Committee, CCIR.

## NICAM system outline

In the NICAM system digitised analogue sound signals are grouped into **data blocks** of 704 bits each. The data blocks are organised in a 1 ms **frame** structure as shown in Fig. 16.1. Each data block is preceded by a **frame alignment** word (FAW) to inform the receiver of the start of each frame. The total frame is then used to modulate a 6.552 MHz carrier which falls just outside the normal 6 MHz f.m. sound but remains within the total TV channel bandwidth of 8 MHz. For stereo transmission, the two sound channels are multiplexed, digitised and transmitted in turn.

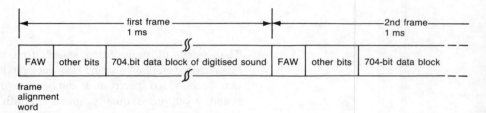

**Fig. 16.1** NICAM 1 ms frame structure

The basic outline of the NICAM stereo system is shown in Fig. 16.2. The two analogue sound channels, A and B, are pre-emphasised before going into an analogue-to-digital converter. Groups of 32 samples of each channel are grouped together to form the basic **data segment** of the system. They are then digitised segment by segment and sample by sample into 14-bit codes using a sampling rate of 32 kHz. This is followed by a 14-to-10 companding network which compresses the 14-bit codes into 10 bits without any significant loss of quality. The error detection parity bit is then added resulting in 11-bit samples. Next, the channel data segments are organised into data blocks. Each data block consists of two 32 × 11-bit sample segments, one from each channel, a total of

$$2 \times 32 \times 11 = 704 \text{ bits.}$$

These 704-bit chunks of data form the basic block (sound + parity) of the NICAM broadcast data frame. Each frame consists of a total of 728 bits as follows:

704 bits for 64 × 11-bit-samples and
24 bits for frame alignment and operation control.

The time duration of each frame is 1 ms resulting in a bit rate of

$$\text{bit rate} = 728/1 \text{ ms} = 728 \text{ kbit/s.}$$

Framing is followed by interleaving and scrambling. Interleaving is necessary to ensure that error bursts are distributed among several samples which are far apart. Scrambling avoids the uneven distribution of energy which follows the process of modulation. The companded, interleaved and scrambled data frame is then used to modulate a subcarrier which is 6.552 MHz above the vision carrier as shown in Fig.

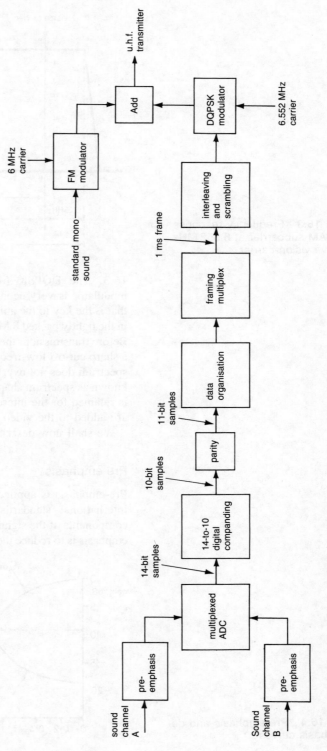

**Fig. 16.2**  Basic outline of NICAM transmitter

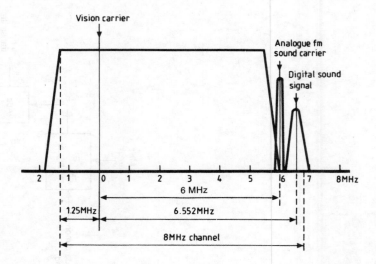

**Fig. 16.3**  Frequency response with NICAM subcarrier at 6.552 MHz above vision carrier

16.3. The DQPSK (differential quadrature phase shift keying) modulator is very economical in bandwidth requirements, a factor that is the key to the ability of NICAM to squeeze yet another signal in the tightly packed 8 MHz bandwidth allocated for each TV channel. Before transmission, the modulated NICAM carrier is passed through a sharp cut-off low-frequency filter to ensure the NICAM frequency spectrum does not overlap with the analogue f.m. carrier, a process known as spectrum shaping. The analogue 6 MHz f.m. sound carrier is retained for the interests of compatibility and both sound carriers are added to the video signal for u.h.f. transmission.

We shall now describe the system in detail.

## Pre-emphasis

Pre-emphasis is applied to each audio channel in accordance with international standards to give a boost to the high-frequency components of the signal as shown in Fig. 16.4. The purpose of pre-emphasis is to reduce the noise level which resides mainly at the high-

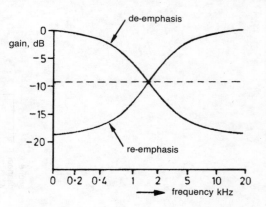

**Fig. 16.4**  Pre-emphasis and de-emphasis curves

frequency end. Pre-emphasis is applied either while the sound signal is in analogue form or by means of digital filters while it is in a digitised form. At the receiving end, the balance between the strength of the low and high-frequencies is restored by a complementary de-emphasis of the signal which reduces the amplitude of the high-frequency components.

## Analogue-to-digital conversion

Studies have shown that an audio bandwidth of 15 kHz is quite adequate for good quality broadcasting to the home. Sampling a 15 kHz audio signal therefore requires a minimum sampling frequency of $15 \times 2 = 30$ kHz (the Nyquist rate). However, to prevent aliasing and its consequential distortion which occurs when the lower sideband of the sampling frequency ($30/2 = 15$ kHz) overlaps with the upper end of the audio frequency (also 15 kHz), a higher sampling rate, namely 32 kHz, is used. For this purpose a filter with a very sharp cut-off at 15 kHz is inserted in the audio path before the sampling process.

Sampling of the two channels is carried out simultaneously. A group of 32 samples of one channel is then converted sample by sample into a 14-bit coded word followed by another group of 32 samples of the second channel and so on. The two's complement method of representing binary numbers is used, being the most convenient to represent positive and negative excursions. The output of the analogue-to-digital converter thus consists of segments of data representing groups of 32 samples of one channel followed by a second segment representing 32 samples of the other channel and so on.

A 14-bit digitiser provides 16,384 quantum levels which is adequate for high-quality sound reproduction. If fewer than 14 bits are used, the quantising error can become audible in the form of a 'gritty' quality for low level signals, an effect known as **granular distortion**.

## 14-to-10 digital companding

The use of 32 kHz sampling with a coding accuracy of 14 bits per sample would require a data bit rate of approximately 1 Mbit/s and consequently a very large bandwidth which could not be accommodated within a single TV channel. For this reason near instantaneous digital companding is used which enables the number of bits per sample to be reduced from 14 to 10 with virtually no degradation in the quality of sound reproduction. Consequently the data bit rate of the system is markedly reduced.

Unlike analogue companding described earlier which has the aim of improving the signal-to-noise ratio, the purpose of digital companding is to reduce the number of bits per sample and hence the data bit rate. Furthermore because all the operations of digital companding are performed in digital form, the compressor at the transmitting coding stage and the expander at the encoder receiving stage can be matched precisely without the mistracking that is associated with analogue companding.

The companding technique used in NICAM is based on the fact that the significance of each bit of a binary code depends on the sound level which the particular sample code represents. For instance assuming a peak analogue input of 1 V, then with a 14-bit code the quantum step is given by

$$\text{Quantum step} = 1\,\text{V/quantum levels} = 1\,\text{V}/16384 = 61\,\mu\text{V}$$

This is the value of the least significant bit. The second least significant bit has a value of $2 \times 16 = 32\,\mu\text{V}$ and so on. It can readily be seen that for a loud sound, i.e. a high amplitude sample, say 500 mV or over, the effect of the three or four least significant bits is imperceptible and may be neglected. However, for delicate or quiet passages with sample amplitudes in the region of a few hundred $\mu$V, the least significant bits are all important.

NICAM companding reduces the 14-bit sample codes to 10-bit codes in such a way that for low level signals, the receiver is able to re-create the original 14-bit samples and for high amplitude signals between one and four least significant bits are discarded as irrelevant.

Each segment of 32 successive audio samples is investigated to find

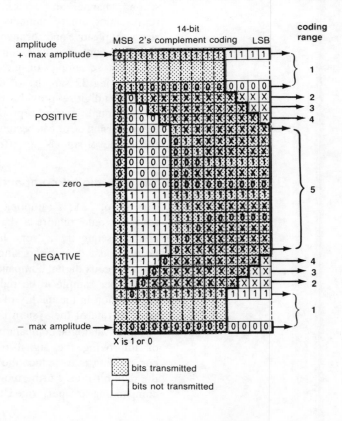

**Fig. 16.5** Coding of companded sound signals

the largest sample in that segment. The amplitude of this sample is then used to indicate the audio strength of the whole segment in five coding ranges as shown in Fig. 16.5. Coding range 1 represents a segment where the largest sample falls between the maximum amplitude and half the maximum amplitude; range 2 from half to quarter maximum amplitude; range 3 from quarter to 1/8th; range 4 from 1/8th to 1/16th and range 5 represents 1/16th of maximum amplitude to zero or silence. The shaded bits in Fig. 16.5 show the bits actually transmitted for each range. In each case the most significant bit, the 14th, being the sign bit, is retained to indicate a positive or negative value. The 13th bit is discarded if it is the same as the 14th; the 12th is likewise discarded if it is the same as the 13th and 14th and similarly with the 11th and 10th bits. Where high order bits are discarded, NICAM provides a labelling technique known as **scale-factor coding** which enables the missing bits to be reconstituted at the receiver. When the discarding of the high order bits is completed, coded samples of between 10 and 14 bits are left depending on the sequence of the high order bits. Where a code has more than 10 bits a sufficient number of bits are removed starting from the least significant bit upwards to reduce the size of the code to 10 bits.

It follows, therefore, that for a segment of 32 samples falling in the largest amplitude range, range 1, the four least significant bits of each sample are discarded and lost for ever. In the case of segments falling in range 2, the next to the most significant bit, the 13th bit of each sample, is discarded along with the three least significant bits. While the three least significant bits are lost, the 13th bit is reconstituted at the receiver since it always has the same value as the most significant bit, and so on for ranges 3, 4 and 5.

## Parity, protection and scale factors

The next stage is the addition of the parity bit to each sample code resulting in an 11-bit word. One parity bit is added to the 10-bit sample to check the six most significant bits for the presence of errors. The remaining bits, the five least significant, are transmitted without a parity check. Even parity is used for the group formed by the six most significant bits. Subsequently, the parity bits are modified to introduce greater error protection and correction as well as coding range information.

The decoder at the receiving end needs to know of the number of high order bits that have been discarded so that they may be re-inserted. This is carried out by labelling each coding range with a code known as the scale factor. The scale factor is a three-bit code which informs the decoder of the number of discarded high order bits. To save on bandwidth requirement, this information is conveyed without the use of additional bits. Instead the information is inserted by modifying the parity bits, a technique known as **signalling-in-parity**.

The principle of operation of the signalling-in-parity technique is to take a group of nine samples within a basic 32 sample segment and use it to indicate one bit of the scale-factor. Two other groups of nine samples within the same basic segment are used to indicate the other two bits of the scale-factor. If it is required to set a scale factor bit to 0, then the group of nine samples are allocated even parity. Conversely, odd parity is used to set the scale factor bit to 1. For instance, assuming the number of missing MSBs is 4, then a scale factor of 011 is necessary. The first group of nine samples are given odd parity to represent the LSB (logic 1) of the scale factor and the parity bit of each sample in the group is then chosen accordingly. The second group of nine samples are also given odd parity to represent the second bit (logic 1) of the scale factor. The third group of nine samples is given even parity representing the MSB (logic 0) of the scale factor. At the receiving end, the decoder checks each sample for parity in the normal way, compares the results with the transmitted parity bit of each group of nine samples and extracts the three-bit scale factor. This process also restores the original parity bit for the six most significant bits. Assuming there are no errors due to transmission, the decoder deduces the type of parity, even or odd, used by the transmitter for each group of nine samples and hence the relevant scale bit. In cases of bit error in the coded samples, the decoder uses what is known as majority-decision logic in which it accepts the parity indication of the majority of the group of nine samples and disregards the minority. This technique is very effective because a mistake in a scale factor bit can take place only if more than four of the group of nine samples suffer errors simultaneously, something that is highly unlikely under normal reception conditions.

Table 16.1 shows the scale factor for each coding range. It will be seen that coding range 5 is divided into three different protection ranges. This is because the scale factor codes are used to represent seven protection ranges, also shown in the table. An eighth protection range is not employed in order to keep NICAM compatible with MAC/packet systems for satellite transmission. While the coding range informs the receiver of the number of high order bits that have been compressed and not transmitted, the protection range provides information of the number of high order bits that are the same. For example, in protection range 3, corresponding to coding range 3, the three most significant bits should all be the same (Fig. 16.5) and in protection range 6, the six most significant bits are the same and so on. This makes it possible for the receiver to identify errors and correct them even if the parity check indicates no error.

### Framing multiplex

The data emerging from the analogue-to-digital converter is in the form of 352-bit segments. Each segment consists of 32 × 11-bit samples: A1-A32 for channel A and B1-B32 for channel B, as shown

**Table 16.1**

| Coding range | Scale factor | Protection range | No. of MSBs same |
|---|---|---|---|
| 1 | 1 1 1 | 1 | None |
| 2 | 1 1 0 | 2 | 2 |
| 3 | 1 0 1 | 3 | 3 |
| 4 | 0 1 1 | 4 | 4 |
|  | 1 0 0 | 5 | 5 |
| 5 | 0 1 0 | 6 | 6 |
|  | 0 0 1 or | 7 | 7 or over |
|  | 0 0 0 |  |  |

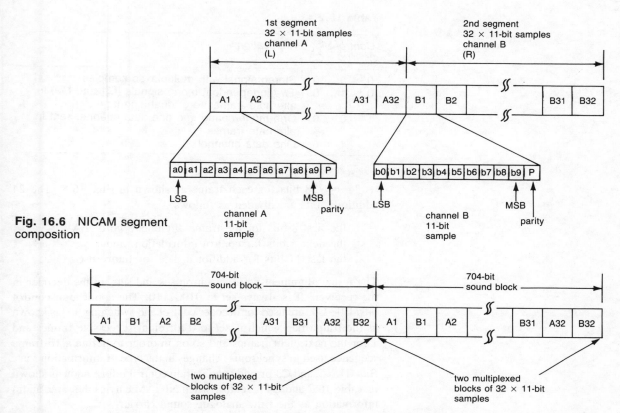

**Fig. 16.6** NICAM segment composition

**Fig. 16.7** NICAM block composition

in Fig. 16.6. Before framing occurs the data stream is organised into blocks each of which is composed of two segments, one from each channel which in the case of stereo sound broadcasting are multiplexed as shown in Fig. 16.7. Each sound block is then preceded by an additional 24 bits for identification and control to give a total of 704

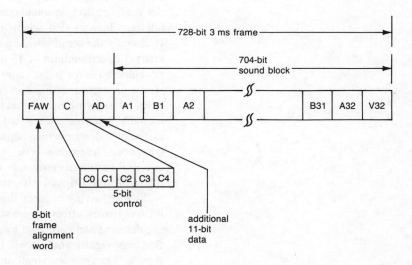

**Fig. 16.8** Structure of a 728-bit NICAM frame

**Table 16.2**

| Control bits | | | Application |
|---|---|---|---|
| C1 | C2 | C3 | |
| 0 | 0 | 0 | Stereo signal with multiplexed samples |
| 0 | 1 | 0 | Two independent mono signals (M1 and M2) in alternate frames, e.g. dual language |
| 1 | 0 | 0 | One mono sound and one data channel sent in alternate frames |
| 1 | 1 | 0 | One data channel |

+ 24 = 728 bits for each frame as shown in Fig. 16.8. The 24 additional bits are divided as follows:

> the first 8 bits for the frame alignment word, FAW
> the next 5 bits for control information, and
> the last 11 bits for additional data for future use

The frame alignment word synchronises and sets up the decoder in the receiver. It is always set to 01001110. The application control bits, C0–C4, are used for decoder control and switching. C0 is known as the frame flag which is set to 0 for eight successive frames and 1 for the next eight frames and so on in order to define a 16-frame sequence used to synchronise changes in the type of information sent. Bits C1, C2 and C3 provide application control information as shown in Table 16.2 and C4 is set to 1 when NICAM carries the same audio information as the f.m. analogue sound carrier.

## Bit interleaving

Bit interleaving is applied to the 704-bit sound block in order to minimise the effect of multiple bit error known as error burst caused by transient noise which may corrupt a number of adjacent bits with devastating effect on sound quality. NICAM bit interleaving separates adjacent bits so that when the data stream is finally transmitted (following the scrambling process) they are at least 16 clock cycles apart (i.e. a minimum of 15 other bits occur between them). Thus, provided an error burst spans fewer than 16 bits, it will spread as single bit errors in different samples.

Bit interleaving is achieved by writing the 704-bit sound block into memory locations of a RAM chip and then reading them out in a different sequence which separates adjacent bits by a predetermined bit space. The readout order is stored in a read only memory known as a ROM **address-sequencer** which is also used in the decoding stage to restore the original bit pattern.

Bit interleaving ensures that the most likely errors are single bit errors. Errors affecting the six most significant bits of any sample are detected and corrected by the parity bit. Errors in the remaining five least significant bits will not be detected, but should they occur they will cause very small annoyance to the listener.

## Scrambling

Before modulation, the bit stream is scrambled to make the signal appear like random sound thus dispersing the energy and reduce further the likelihood of interference with the analogue f.m. sound or video signal. The frame alignment word (FAW) is not scrambled since this is needed to synchronise the transmitter with the receiver. Total random scattering is not possible because there is no way of de-scrambling the bits back into their original order at the receiver. However, a pseudo-random scattering can be achieved using a **pseudo-random sequence generator** (PRSG) which produces the same result as total random distribution. The output of the PRSG is predictable and may be repeated at the start of each frame. At the receiving end, a reciprocal process takes place which de-scrambles the data bits back into their original form.

## DQPSK modulation

A digital signal has only two states, 1 and 0, and when it is used to modulate a carrier, only two states of the carrier amplitude, frequency or phase, are necessary to convey the digital information. In terms of bandwidth, the most economical form of modulation is phase modulation known as phase-shift keying (PSK) in which the carrier frequency remains constant while its phase changes in discrete phase states in accordance with the logic state of the data bit. Binary PSK is a two-phase modulation technique in which the carrier is transmitted with a reference phase of 0° to indicate a logic 1 and a phase of 180° to indicate logic 0.

Quadrature phase-shift keying (QPSK) (also known as four-phase PSK) has four phase settings: a reference 0° phase, 90°, 180° and 270°. Each setting represents a digital state. The advantage of this type of modulation is its ability to send twice as much information as the binary PSK for the same bandwidth.

Differential phase-shift keying (DPSK) has no specific reference phase. The phase shift incates if the current bit is different from the previous bit. The phase reference therefore is the previously transmitted signal phase. The advantage of this is that the receiver as well as the transmitter does not have to maintain an absolute phase reference with which the phase of the received signal is compared.

The differential quadrature phase-shift keying (DQPSK) technique used in NICAM combines the advantages of the QPSK on the one hand and those of the DPSK technique on the other. Using a serial-to-parallel converter, the serial bit stream is first converted into a two-bit parallel format. The instantaneous states of each pair of bits known as dibits can take one of four combinations, namely 00, 01, 10 and 11. Each of these combinations changes the phase of the carrier from its previous setting by a different angle as shown in Table 16.3. The four 2-bit data combinations are thus represented by four different phase changes. For example data 00 is represented by no change in

**Table 16.3**

| Input bits | Phase change |
|---|---|
| 0  0 | no change |
| 0  1 | − 90° |
| 1  0 | −180° |
| 1  1 | −270° |

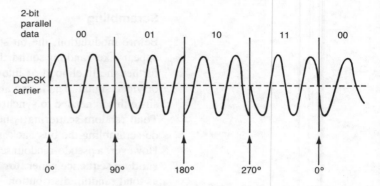

Fig. 16.9   DQPSK carrier waveform

the phase of the carrier and 11 is represented by a 270° phase change as shown in Fig. 16.9. Since the serial stream is now converted to a two-bit parallel form, the bit rate is reduced by half, from 728 kbit/s to 364 kbit/s which explains the saving in bandwidth.

## The NICAM receiver

At the receiver, the tuner converts the vision carrier and the f.m. sound inter-carrier to an i.f. of 39.5 MHz and 33.5 MHz respectively in the normal way. The NICAM carrier being 6.552 MHz away from the vision carrier is converted to an intermediate frequency of

$$\text{NICAM i.f.} = 39.5 - 6.552 = 32.948 \text{ MHz or } 32.95 \text{ MHz.}$$

This is demodulated by a DQPSK detector and applied to the NICAM decoder which reverses the processes carried out at the transmitter to recreate the 14-bit sample code words for each channel. This is then followed by a digital-to-analogue converter which reproduces the original analogue two-channel, left and right sound waveforms.

The basic elements of NICAM sound reception in a TV receiver is shown in Fig. 16.10. Following the tuner, a special surface acoustic wave filter (SAWF) provides separate vision and sound i.f. outputs. A sharp cut-off removes the two sound i.f.s, 33.5 MHz for mono and 32.95 MHz for NICAM, from the vision 39.5 MHz carrier. The SAW

Fig. 16.10   Basic elements of NICAM sound receiver

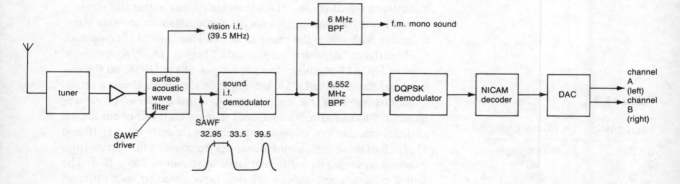

filter provides a separate path for the f.m. and NICAM carrier i.f.s. It also provides for a very narrow peak at 39.5 MHz. In the sound i.f. demodulator, the 39.5 MHz pilot frequency is used to beat with the f.m. sound i.f and with the NICAM i.f. to produce 6 MHz f.m. and 6.552 MHz DQPSK carriers. Sharply tuned filters are then used to separate the two sound carriers. The f.m. carrier goes to a conventional f.m. processing channel for mono sound and the 6.552 MHz NICAM phase modulated carrier goes to the NICAM processing section. This consists of three basic parts. The DQPSK decoder recovers the 728 kbit/s serial data stream from the 6.552 MHz carrier. The NICAM decoder de-scrambles, de-interleaves, corrects and expands the data stream back into 14-bit sample code words. Finally, the digital-to-analogue converter reproduces the original analogue signals for each channel.

### The DQPSK decoder

The phase demodulator or detector works on the same principles as a f.m. detector in which a variation in phase (or frequency) produces a variation in the d.c. output. In the case of two-phase modulation, the d.c. output of the detector has two distinct values representing logic 1 and logic 0. However, in the case of quadrature, i.e. four-phase modulation, the output of the detector is ambiguous. The same output for a 90° phase shift is obtained as that for a phase shift of 270°. Similarly for phase shifts of 0° and 180°. In order to resolve the ambiguities, a second phase detector operating in quadrature (90°) is used. Fig. 16.11 shows the main elements of a DQPSK demodulator using an in-phase phase detector (PDI) and a quadrature phase detector (PDQ). The outputs from the two phase detectors, data I and Q, are fed into a data recovery circuit which reproduces the original 728-bit serial data stream. The 6.552 MHz reference carrier frequency is

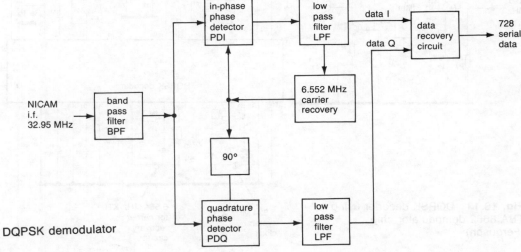

**Fig. 16.11**   DQPSK demodulator elements

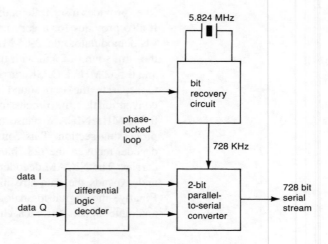

**Fig. 16.12**   Data recovery circuit

generated by a carrier recovery circuit which includes a crystal tuned voltage controlled oscillator and a phase-locked loop.

The main elements of a data recovery circuit is shown in Fig. 16.12 in which the bit recovery circuit includes a second PLL locked to the bit rate of 728 kHz. In order to ensure a 'clean' bit rate clock, a master system clock which is a multiple of the bit rate is used. In this case a clock frequency of 5.824 MHz is used. The bit rate is then retrieved by dividing the master system clock by eight. The I and Q data from the DQPSK detector are fed into a differential logic decoder which produces the correponding two-bit parallel data. The pairs of parallel data are then fed into a parallel-to-serial converter which reconstructs the original 728-bit serial stream before going to the NICAM decoder.

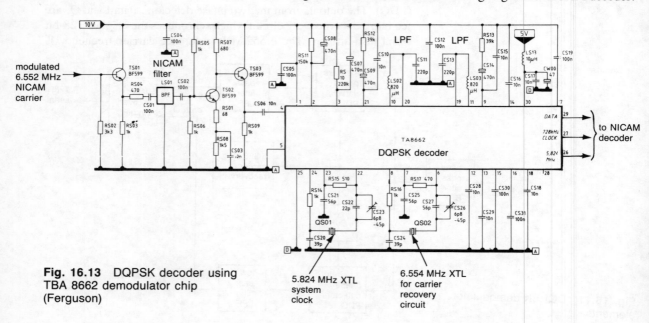

**Fig. 16.13**   DQPSK decoder using TBA 8662 demodulator chip (Ferguson)

Practical DQPSK decoders are available in i.c. packages such as the TA8662N and the TDA8732. They incorporate a second phase detector driven by the Q data which generates a muting signal to turn the f.m. mono sound on and off depending upon the presence or otherwise of the 6.552 MHz NICAM carrier. A practical DQPSK decoder circuit using the TA8662 chip is shown in Fig. 16.13 in which two chassis levels are available, a D chassis for digital signals and an A chassis for analogue signals. Transistor TS01 is a filter driver and TS02/TS03 form a two-stage NICAM i.f. amplifier. The 6.552 MHz carrier enters at pin 4 and the outputs are at pin 29 (728-bit data stream), pin 21 (728 kHz clock) and pin 26 (5.824 MHz system clock). The system clock 5.824 MHz crystal QS01 and the 6.552 MHz crystal QS02 form part of the bit and carrier recovery circuits respectively. The I and Q low-pass filters are connected to pins 11 and 10 respectively.

## NICAM decoder

The NICAM decoder, which is sometimes known as the NICAM multiplexer, de-scrambles, de-interleaves and re-constitutes the original 14-bit words. It provides data, ident and clock signals to the digital-to-analogue converter. A simplified block diagram of the decoding process is shown in Fig. 16.14. The encoded data from the DQPSK detector is fed into the frame alignment word (FAW) detector for frame recognition and resetting of the de-scrambler and de-interleaver. The de-scrambled data is then fed into the de-interleaver which reproduces the original dual channel (L and R) data together with a L/R ident signal to select the signal paths as appropriate. De-interleaving is carried out by first writing the data stream into memory cells block by block. The cells are then read out in an order determined

**Fig. 16.14** NICAM decoding process

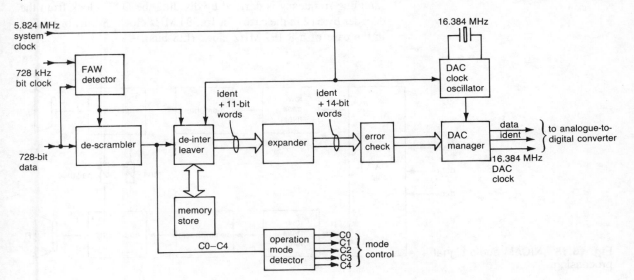

by a programme held in ROM to reproduce the correct order of the bits. The programme contains the complement of the address-sequencer used at the transmitter. The de-scrambled data is also fed to the operation mode detector which decodes control bits C0−C4 and provides information to the expander and other parts of the system in terms of the type of transmission, e.g. stereo, mono or bilingual.

Having restored each 11-bit word (10 + parity) to its correct order, they have to be expanded back to a 14-bit format. This is carried out by an expansion circuit which functions in a complementary manner to the compressor at the transmitter but uses the scale factor embodied in the parity bits to expand the 10-bit sample codes into 14 bits. This is followed by an error check circuit in which the error parity is used to investigate and correct the bit stream. Before leaving the decoder for the digital-to-analogue converter, the data is fed to a DAC manager which organises a three-line bus output consisting of a data bit stream, an ident signal and a DAC clock known as DACOSC. At the converter the DAC clock is subdivided to accurately produce the sampling frequency. There are two three-line ouput bus formats that may be used to feed the DAC: the **S-bus** for converters using 16.384 MHz clock and the **I2S-bus** for converters using 8.192 MHz clock.

## Digital-to-analogue converter

A single digital-to-analogue converter is normally used that works on alternate left and right code words. The most popular type is the integrating DAC. It uses a precision capacitor which is charged by a constant current source for a period determined by the data content of each 14-bit word. The L/R ident signal ensures that the correct channel is selected at any one time. The amplitude of each sample is kept constant between samples by a hold circuit. The 32 kHz sampling frequency is derived by dividing the DAC clock from the decoder by 512 in the case of a 16.384 MHz clock (S-bus) or by 256 in the case of a 8.192 MHz clock (I2S-bus).

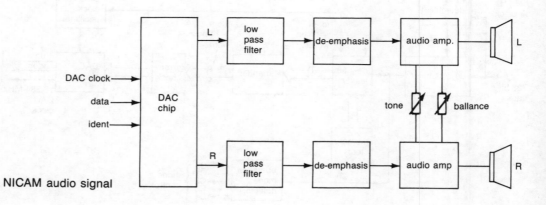

**Fig. 16.15**  NICAM audio signal processing

## Switching arrangements

All modern TV receivers have some complex switching arrangements to implement changes between NICAM stereo, mono or bilingual, f.m. sound and auxiliary sound or video inputs as well as making the sound and video signals available for outside use. Control of the switching network is carried out by the NICAM decoder and other control chips such as a microprocessor unit.

## Audio signal processing

Following the DAC, the analogue signals known as the baseband audio signals first pass through a low-pass filter with a sharp 15 kHz cut-off frequency in order to smooth out the quantising steps and minimise quantising noise in the reconstructed audio signal (Fig. 16.15). This is followed by a de-emphasis network which re-establishes the correct response for each channel and restores the signals to their original audio form ready for tone control and amplification. Two separate hi-fi audio amplifiers available in i.c. packages are used for the L and R channels.

# 17 Microcomputer controlled receivers

The microcomputer, also known as a microcontroller or mini-controller, is a complete microprocessor-based system constructed on a single chip, known as a single-chip computer.

The basic structure of a microprocessor-based system is shown in Fig. 17.1. It consists of four basic elements: microprocessor unit (MPU); memory chips (RAM and ROM); input/output ports and a bus structure. The MPU chip contains all the necessary circuitry to interpret and execute program instructions in terms of data manipulation, logic and arithmetic operations and timing and control. The capacity or bit size of a microprocessor chip is determined by the number of data bits it can handle. A four-bit chip has a four-bit data width and an eight-bit chip has an eight-bit data width and so on. RAM and ROM are two types of memory chips that are normally used. Other types such as PROM, EPROM and EEPROM may also be used. The input/output (I/O) ports provide a link to and from the system with peripheral devices such as keyboards, VDU, and transducers or drive circuitry for stepper motors, LEDs and relays. There are two type of ports, the parallel and serial. The parallel ports consist of a number of bidirectional lines, each of which may be designated as input or output. The serial port provides a two-line (data IN and data OUT) serial interface. The various elements of the system are interconnected by a bus structure. The number of tracks or lines used in a bus is determined by the capacity and complexity of the microprocessor chip. There are three types of buses: the data bus, the address bus and the control bus. The data bus is used to transfer data between the MPU and other elements in the system. The address bus is used to carry the address of memory locations from which data may be retrieved, i.e. READ from memory devices, or to store i.e. WRITE data into memory locations. It is also used to address other elements in the system such as the input/output ports. The control bus carries the control signals of the MPU such as the clock $\Phi$, RESET, read (RD) and write (WR). The number of control lines depends on the microprocessor used and the design of the system. In order to reduce the number of tracks in a bus multiplexing may be used either between groups of lines within a bus or between one bus and another resulting in a single-bus structure as shown in Fig. 17.1.

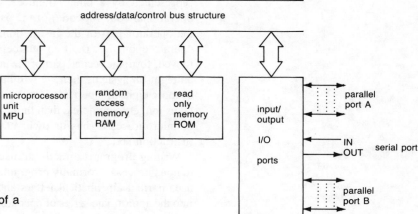

address/data/control bus structure

| microprocessor unit MPU | random access memory RAM | read only memory ROM | input/ output I/O ports |

parallel port A

IN
OUT    serial port

parallel port B

**Fig. 17.1** The basic elements of a microprocessor-based system

The microprocessor chip has a complex architecture which, though it varies from one manufacturer to another, has the following common units:

Arithmetic and logic unit
Timing and control logic
Accumulator and other registers
Instruction decoder
Internal bus

## General operation of the system

The heart of the system, the microprocessor chip, operates on a **fetch and execute** cycle synchronised by the system clock. During the fetch phase, the CPU receives the instruction from the memory location where the program is held and stores it into an internal register known as the instruction register. During the execute phase, the MPU having received the instruction will then decode it and execute it. This is carried out by the MPU generating the necessary timing and control signals for the execution of that particular instruction. The execute phase may involve a simple arithmetic operation, e.g. add or subtract, or a more complex data transfer to or from a memory chip or a peripheral device. When the instruction is completed, the microprocessor then fetches the next instruction and so on.

## The instruction set

The microprocessor performs its tasks in a predetermined sequence known as the program. The program is a series of instructions which breaks down each operation into a number of individual tasks. These instructions are fed into the microprocessor chip in the form of binary digits. An instruction consists of two parts: an **operator** and an **operand**. Each instruction such as ADD or MOVE DATA is represented by a binary number known as the machine code or operational code (**opcode**) of the particular microprocessor. This is the operator part of the instruction. The data that the opcode is to operate upon, i.e. the two numbers to be added or the data to be moved, form the second part of the instruction, the operand. Assuming an eight-bit system, then we will have an eight-bit operator and one or more eight-bit operands. An instruction with a number of operands takes longer to complete than those with fewer operands. Each make of microprocessor has its own set of machine codes known as the instruction set.

Writing programs directly in machine code is a very lengthy and tedious process. Normally programs are written in a language which uses normal alphabetical letters and words. This is then translated into the appropriate series of opcodes. The simplest form of translation is the assembler which employs the **assembly programming** language. In the assembly language each opcode is given a mnemonic name such as EN for Enable, MOV for Move, ANL for Logic AND and INC for Increment.

## Microcomputers

Microcomputers or microcontrollers are complete microprocessor systems on a single chip. They contain the elements of the microprocessor itself as well as RAM, ROM or other memory devices and input/output ports. A variety of microcomputers are available from various manufacturers (Intel 8048/49 and 8051 series, Motorola 6805 and 146805, Texas TMS1000 and Ziloc Z80 series) for use as dedicated computer systems for such applications as car engines, washing machines, VCRs and of course TV receivers. The difference between one type of microprocessor and another lies in the type and size of memory, instruction set, operating speed, number of available input and output lines and data length, e.g. four, eight or 16 bits. Where microcomputers are customised for specific use, they are referred to as **application-specific integrated circuits** (ASICs). In the majority of cases, microcontrollers have their program stored permanently into an internal ROM at the manufacturing stage, a process known as mask programming. Some chips have an internal EPROM available for user programming.

## Microcontroller internal architecture

The basic architecture of an eight-bit microcontroller or minicontroller is shown in Fig. 17.2. The program is held in ROM with a small RAM of between 1−4 k available for data and other external control signals. The timer/counter may be loaded, started, stopped or read by software commands. In TV applications it is used to keep track of the sequence of lines and fields and prompt the controller to carry out certain operations at specific times. Two parallel eight-bit ports

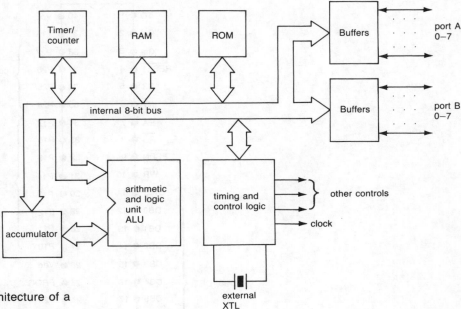

**Fig. 17.2** Internal architecture of a microcontroller

are shown, ports A and B, which may be assigned as inputs or outputs. A serial input/output port may be established by using two lines of the parallel ports, one to receive and the other to transmit serial data. The ALU carries out arithmetic operations such as adding two numbers or performs a logic function such as NAND or NOR on two numbers. The ALU therefore has two inputs, one input for each number. When the ALU operation is completed, the result is stored in the accumulator. The timing and control unit provides the necessary synchronisation of the system through the clock and other control signals. Interconnection between the various units is provided by a single multiplexed eight-bit bus.

Television minicontrollers are based on one or other of the main types of microcomputer. Each TV manufacturer has custom built microcontrollers such as the MAB8400 (Mullard), CCU2000 (ITT), CCU7070 (Fedility), MC6805 (Grundig), FERG01 (Ferguson) and PCF84C640 (Hitachi).

## 8048 minicontroller

The pin connection for the 8048 series microcomputer chip is shown in Fig. 17.3 in which

P10—P17 and P20—P27 are two bidirectional ports,
DB0—DB7 provides access to the internal data bus, it may also be used as a third eight-bit port.
T0 and T1 are two input lines,
Pins 2 and 3 are for clock crystal connections

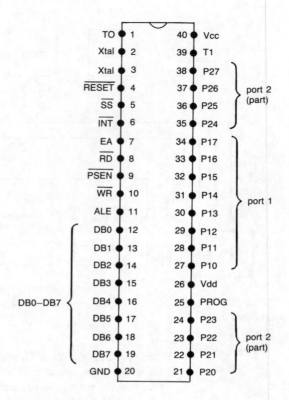

**Fig. 17.3**   8048 minicontroller pin connection

$\overline{\text{INT}}$ and $\overline{\text{RESET}}$ are interrupt and reset inputs. The bars above INT and RESET indicate that these lines are active low, i.e. they become active when at logic 0

Pins 8 and 10 provide active low read and write output control

$\overline{\text{SS}}$ (pin 5) allows single stepping of the program for debugging purposes

$\overline{\text{PSEN}}$ allows external or additional program storage

PROG drives an output expansion chip

ALE (pin 11) is address latch enable for use in conjunction with an external address latch.

The 8048 has a powerful set of 96 instructions, a 1 k ROM and a RAM capacity of 64 bytes ($64 \times 8$ bits). It may be programmed using assembler language. For memory efficiency, each instruction (operator and operand) consists of only one or two bytes.

When used for any particular application, e.g. in a TV receiver, a program is implanted in the microprocessor which assigns each pin a particular function. Microcontrollers may also be modified to include other functions such as tuning and analogue-to-digital conversion. Additional memory space may be added in the form of EEPROM, electrically erasable programmable read only memory.

## TV microcontrollers

A variety of functions can be performed by a microcomputer in a TV receiver including generating test signals and storing parameters and customer adjustments. The microcontroller may be used to perform some or all of the following functions:

front panel keyboard scanning
LED display drive
volume and tone control
audio muting
brightness and saturation control
remote control decoding
switching and control of luma and chroma processing
switching between video, teletext and auxiliary inputs
test signal generation and automatic adjustments
on-screen graphic generation and control
u.h.f. tuner control
analogue-to-digital decoding

A functional block diagram for a TV microcontroller usually known as central control unit, CCU is shown in Fig. 17.4. The microcomputer core circuit controls the other units by an internal bus in accordance with the program stored in the internal ROM. The

**Fig. 17.4** TV microcontroller chip architecture

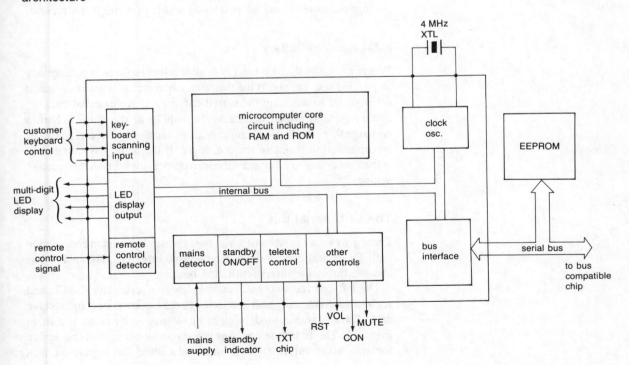

keyboard on the receiver front panel is scanned, i.e. read by a number of I/O port bits designated as input bits. Other bits are assigned to control a multi-digit LED display. A further port bit receives remote control signals and feeds them into a remote control decoder. Channel selection or other adjustments (contrast, saturation, etc.) from either the keyboard or the remote control handset are fed via the internal bus into the microcomputer core circuit which sends the appropriate command signals including those to the multi-digit LED display unit. Control of the receiver may be effected by assigning the various port bits a dedicated function such as keyboard scanning or volume, contrast or teletext control. It may also be operated through a serial bus which connects to other compatible chips in the receiver. A 4 MHz crystal is used to generate the microcontroller clock pulse. Connection to the other units of the receiver is realised by a 2-line or 3-line serial bus. This also connects an EEPROM to the system which provides a non-volatile memory store. Unlike the internal RAM which loses its contents when power is switched off, the EEPROM chip retains its data regardless of the power supply. Furthermore selected cells may be cleared and new data written into the chip. At the manufacturing stage, the EEPROM is used to store the data necessary to customise the receiver for its particular range of facilities, e.g. teletext, NICAM etc., type of transmission system (PAL, NTSC, Secam) and other normal settings such as height, vertical sync. and saturation. Customer's preferences as to contrast, saturation, etc. may also be stored into EEPROM at home. Casual variations on these settings are stored in the internal RAM within the central control unit.

## RAM back-up battery

Where a volatile RAM is used to store receiver settings, it is necessary to provide d.c. supply to the memory when the receiver is switched off in order to maintain the stored data intact. An external back-up battery is used which maintains the supply to the chip. Where a rechargeable battery is employed, a charging circuit must be incorporated to maintain the d.c. level. If the battery is changed, it is then necessary to reprogram the microprocessor with all the receiver settings.

## The CCU serial bus

There are two main types of serial buses which are used in conjunction with TV central control units: the two-line **inter i.c.**, **IIC** or **I²C** bus and the three-line **intermetall**, **IM** bus.

The I²C bus has two bidirectional lines: a serial clock, SCL and serial data, SDA. Any unit connected to the bus may send and receive data. Data is transmitted in eight-bit words or bytes as shown in Fig.17.5. The first byte contains the seven-bit address of the device for which the information is intended, while the eighth bit is a

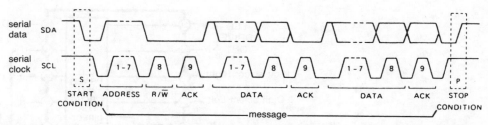

**Fig. 17.5** I²C bus data construction

read/write bit to signify whether the data is required from, or being sent to, the device. A number of data bytes follow, the total number in a message depends on the nature of information being transferred. Each data byte is terminated by an acknowledge (ACK) bit. Like all other bits, the ACK bit has a related clock pulse on the clock line as shown. The first byte of any data transfer is preceded by a start condition and is terminated by a stop condition. To ensure that two devices do not use the bus simultaneously, an arbitration logic system is used. The clock which operates only when data is transferred has a variable speed. Data may then be sent at a slow or a fast rate of up to 100 kbit/s.

The Intermetall bus has three lines: Ident I, Clock C and Data D. Both the ident and the clock lines are unidirectional between the microcontroller and the other peripheral devices. The data line is bidirectional. The start of transmission is indicated by the ident line going low (Fig. 17.6). An eight-bit address is sent along the data line. At the end of eight clock cycles, the I line goes high indicating the start of data transmission. Data is then transmitted along the D line for eight (or 16) clock cycles for an eight-bit (or 16-bit) data word at the end of which the I line goes low again indicating the end of data transmission.

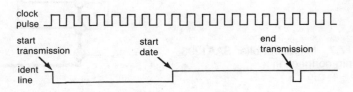

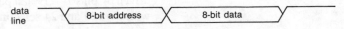

**Fig. 17.6** Intermetall bus lines

Both buses may be used simultaneously in a single receiver to provide connections with different sections of the receiver. Ferguson's ICC5 chassis for instance uses four different buses, IM, I²C, tuning and Thomson for channel selection and analogue control, teletext and graphics, u.h.f. tuner and video processing respectively. Manufacturers have available a number of peripheral chips including tuner interfaces, EEPROMs, and ADCs and TV processing chips for operation with I²C or IM buses.

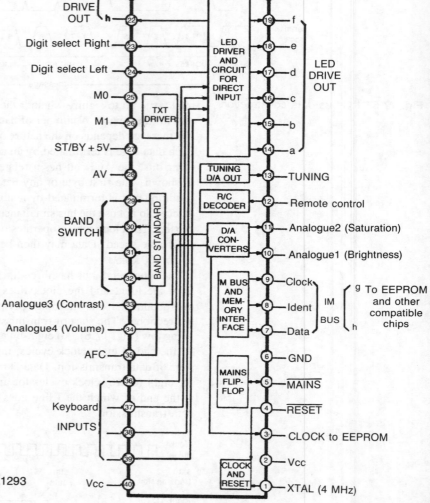

**Fig. 17.7** Microcontroller SAA1293 chip pin connection

The pin connections for a practical microcontroller chip (SAA1293) are shown in Fig. 17.7. A two-digit eight-segment front display is driven by pins 14–19 and pins 21–25. The two digits are multiplexed with pins 23 and 24 selecting each digit in turn. The eight segments a–h of each digit are then driven by pins 14–19 and pins 21 and 22. The input to the LED drive circuit is derived directly from the keyboard (pins 36–39) on the front panel or via remote control (pin 12). Four analogue output control signals are provided at pins 10, 11, 33 and 34 for brightness, colour saturation, contrast and volume. Pins 7, 8 and 9 provide the data, ident and clock lines for an IM bus to interface with an external EEPROM and other compatible chips. Pins 29–32 provide a facility for selecting different u.h.f. bands and transmission standards to customise the receiver for use in different

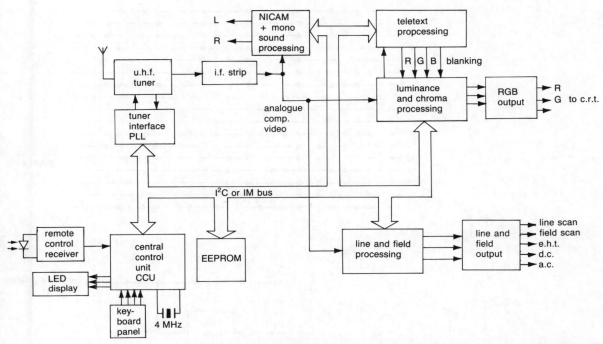

**Fig. 17.8** Microcomputer controlled TV receiver

countries. Such customisation is carried out by software programming of the EEPROM using parameters stored in the microcontroller's internal ROM.

Figure 17.8 shows a block diagram of microcomputer controlled TV receiver employing a single-bus structure.

### On screen display (OSD)

The purpose of OSD is to give visual indication on the TV screen when any function is requested and its state. The display contains characters and numbers arranged in rows along the screen. Each row occupies a number of lines depending on the size of the displayed characters. Assuming a 5 × 7 dot format, then each display line of characters will occupy seven scanning lines as shown in Fig. 17.9. Assuming a non-interlaced system, the process of scanning involves the electron beam sweeping across the first dot matrix row of all the characters in the first display line displaying the appropriate dots along that line scan. This is then followed by the second matrix row and so on. The video signal thus consists of the first row of matrix dots for each successive character, followed by the next row and the next up to the seventh. The video signal of such a display has two levels only, white and black, representing the presence or absence of the dots along each scan line.

The principal elements of an OSD system are shown in Fig. 17.10. Character generation is carried out by a dedicated chip, IC1, under the control of a microcomputer. The character generator contains a

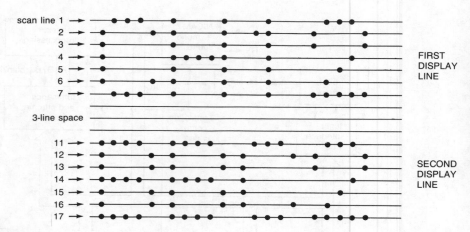

**Fig. 17.9** Character display on TV screen

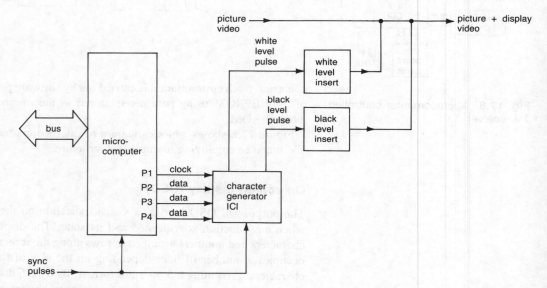

**Fig. 17.10** On screen display, OSD system

code for each character that may be displayed. To display a character, the code is recalled by the microcomputer and placed in an appropriate location in a memory map within the chip itself. The precise location is determined by the position of the character on the screen. For each field, the microcomputer causes the character codes to be retrieved from the memory map in the correct order. Each code generates a set of black and white level pulses which correspond to the luminance content of each scan line. These pulses are then fed into black and white level insert switches which connect the video line to the

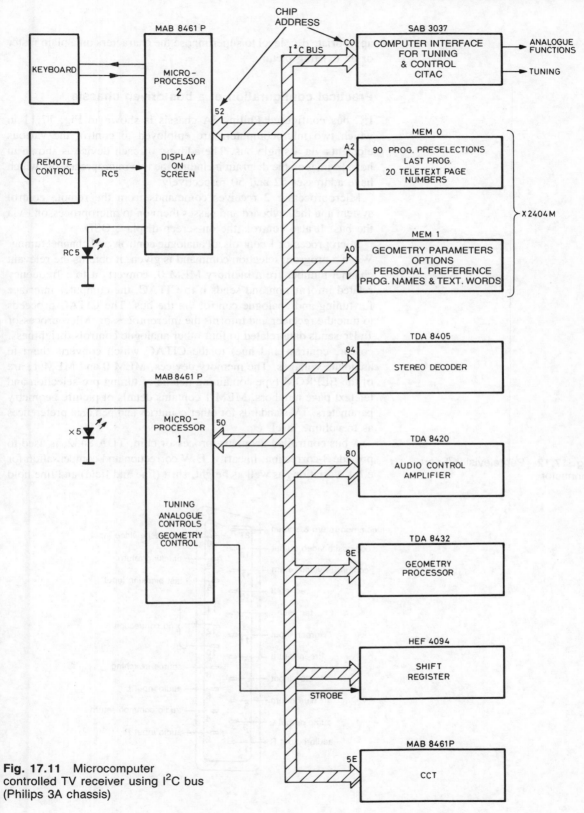

**Fig. 17.11** Microcomputer controlled TV receiver using I²C bus (Philips 3A chassis)

appropriate d.c. level to superimpose the characters on a plain raster or an existing picture.

## Practical configuration of a bus driven chassis

$I^2C$ bus configured Philips 3A chassis is shown in Fig. 17.11 in which two microcomputers are employed to control the various elements via a single bus. The address of each device is shown in hexadecimal on the diagram including the two microprocessors which have addresses 52 and 50 respectively.

Microprocessor 2 receives commands from the remote control system and the keyboard and passes them on to microprocessor 1 via the bus. It also controls the on-screen display, OSD.

Microprocessor 1 controls all analogue controls and channel tuning. When a program selection command is given, it obtains the relevant channel number from memory MEM 0, converts it to a frequency related information and sends it to CITAC, the computer interface for tuning and analogue control via the bus. The CITAC proceeds to tune the receiver and informs the microprocessor. Microprocessor 1 also sends data related to four other analogue controls (brightness, colour, contrast and hue) to the CITAC which converts them to analogue voltages. The memory devices, MEM 0 and MEM 1, are of the EEPROM type containing details of tuning pre-selection and teletext page numbers. MEM 1 contains details of picture geometry parameters, TV standards for other countries and personal preferences as to volume level, etc.

A bus controlled geometry processor chip, TDA 8432, is used to provide S-correction, linearity, E-W correction and compensation for e.h.t. variations as well as height, shift (line and field) and line hold

**Fig. 17.12**   Peritelevision/Scart connector

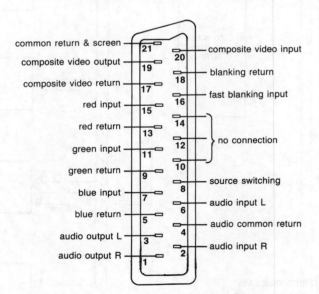

controls. The geometry processor chip receives information from microprocessor 1 via the $I^2C$ bus which enables it to carry out twelve picture geometry functions.

## Peritelevision/Scart connector

Modern TV receivers are designed to receive direct video input from external sources such as a home computer or a video recorder thus avoiding the tuner/i.f. stage. These sets are fitted with a Peritelevision (peripheral television) or Scart connector socket. The Peritelevision connector is a European standard, hence the name Euroconnector. It allows direct input and output of composite video, RGB analogue signals, teletext data and mono and stereo sound. The pin assignment of a Peritelevision/Scart connector is shown in Fig. 17.12. A Peritelevision or Scart interface chip is required to connect the various inputs and output to the relevant parts of the receiver.

# 18 Remote control

The use of remote control is now common to almost all TV receivers. Very early remote control systems used long cables to connect to the receiver. This was followed by the use of visible light from a torch which activated a sensor in the receiver. Next came the ultrasonic system which provided additional facilities and improved performance. Remote control came into its own by the introduction of infrared systems and today they are beginning to resemble data transfer links employing microcomputers at both the transmitter and receiver.

## Remote control system

The basic block diagram of a remote control (RC) system is shown in Fig. 18.1. The keyboard consists of a number of press button contacts, one for each command. When one key is operated, the encoder generates a coded signal which represents the particular selected control key. There are two types of encoder: the static and the scanning encoders. The **static encoder** produces an output when two i.c. pins are shorted by pressing a key. The **scanning encoder** on the other hand contains a program which interrogates the keyboard to identify the closed key. The encoded signals are transmitted as ultrasonic or infrared waves via a transducer diode, DT. The encoded signal is received by sensing diode DS, decoded and the appropriate control is then activated.

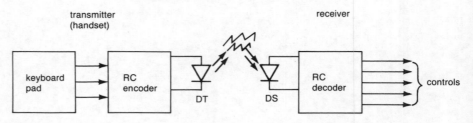

**Fig. 18.1** The basic blocks of a remote control system

## Remote control transmitter

The basic arrangement for a remote control transmitter (handset) using a static encoder is shown in Fig. 18.2 in which a 4 × 4 matrix key

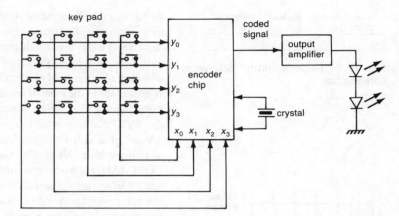

key pad

coded
signal

$y_0$

$y_1$

encoder
chip

$y_2$

$y_3$

output
amplifier

crystal

$x_0$ $x_1$ $x_2$ $x_3$

**Fig. 18.2** Remote control
transmitter

pad is used. The key pad consists of four vertical wires ($x_0$–$x_3$) and four horizontal wires ($y_0$–$y_3$). At each of the 16 cross-points is a push button keyswitch which, when pressed, makes a connection between a vertical and a corresponding horizontal line. Two i.c. pins are thus shorted causing a unique coded signal to be generated which, after amplification, is transmitted by the diode transducer. The number of control keys may be increased by using a larger matrix such as 4 × 8 (32 keys) or 8 × 8 (64 keys) and so on.

## Ultrasonic encoding

The ultrasonic encoder contains a crystal controlled oscillator and a variable frequency divider. When a key is selected, a multi-bit word is generated which determines the setting of the variable divider and hence the frequency of the transmitted ultrasonic wave. The frequency range of ultrasonic transmission is limited and hence the number of commands that may be transmitted by such a system is also limited. Ultrasonic systems have a number of other drawbacks such as spurious responses to rattling keys and coins and even chattering budgerigars. Reflections from walls and other close objects cause confusion at the receiving end and ultimate malfunction of the system. For these reasons, modern remote control systems employ infrared transmission which because of its high velocity removes the problems associated with reflections. Furthermore, because it employs digital coded transmission, infrared remote control provides a far greater number of functions.

## Infrared encoding

The main function of the infrared (IR) encoder chip is to convert a specific $x$–$y$ matrix selection into a corresponding serial data word to drive the IR light-emitting diode. The data word is continuously repeated while the button of the key pad remains pressed. The data word consists of four basic parts as shown in Fig. 18.3. The data

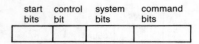

**Fig. 18.3** Remote control data word construction

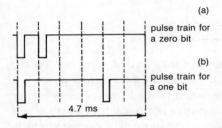

**Fig. 18.4** Pulse-position modulation used by SAA5000 chip

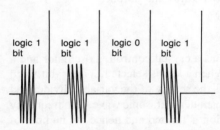

**Fig. 18.5** Amplitude modulation of infrared data

word begins with constant time reference START bits which are used to synchronise the receiver to the transmitter. This is followed by the CONTROL bit which changes its logic level, i.e. toggles with each new switching contact of the keypad. This informs the receiver whether a button has been held down or pressed a second time which is important in the case of commands where the same digit is repeated e.g. channel 11 or teletext page 222. The control bit is followed by the SYSTEM bits which define the device being addressed, e.g. a TV set or a video cassette recorder. This is usually carried out by a two-position VCR-TV switch on the key pad. Finally the COMMAND bits are transmitted. They instruct the receiver as to the setting of various controls. The coding technique and the bit size of the component parts of the data word differ from one manufacturer to another. In remote control systems which control a TV receiver only, the SYSTEM bits may be dispensed with and, where the number of channels does not exceed nine, the CONTROL bits may also be dispensed with leaving START (also known as FRAMING) and COMMAND bits only.

Before transmission the data word has to be modulated. This is necessary because of the characteristic of the infrared transducer diode which, given a stream of similar pulses, would be continuously on and off resulting in a very heavy current drain on the battery which effectively turns the transmitter off. Two types of modulation are used: pulse position and amplitude modulation. The SAA5000 remote control chip uses pulse position modulation (PPM) which separates the pulses thus improving the duty cycle of the IR diode and reducing power consumption. Each logic level is given a five-bit code as shown in Fig. 18.4: a zero bit is given the code shown in (a) and a logic 1 bit is given the code shown in (b). Modern encoders use a constant frequency (in the region of 36 kHz) to amplitude modulate the pulse train. The result is the series of high frequency bursts shown in Fig. 18.5. with each burst representing a logic 1 bit.

## Scanning encoders

Scanning is performed by first taking vertical lines $x_0-x_3$ (Fig. 18.2) to logic 1 and then sequentially turning horizontal lines $y_0-y_3$ on and off. When a closed key is detected, the appropriate bits of the data word are generated. The scanning process commences as soon as a key is pressed and before the START bits are initiated.

## Practical infrared transmitter

A practical remote IR transmitter circuit using a scanning encoder is shown in Fig. 18.6. The coded pulse pattern is derived from the system clock generated by a crystal controlled oscillator operating at a frequency of 72 kHz. The keyboard consists of two matrices: the X-Y matrix consists of two groups of eight terminations on the

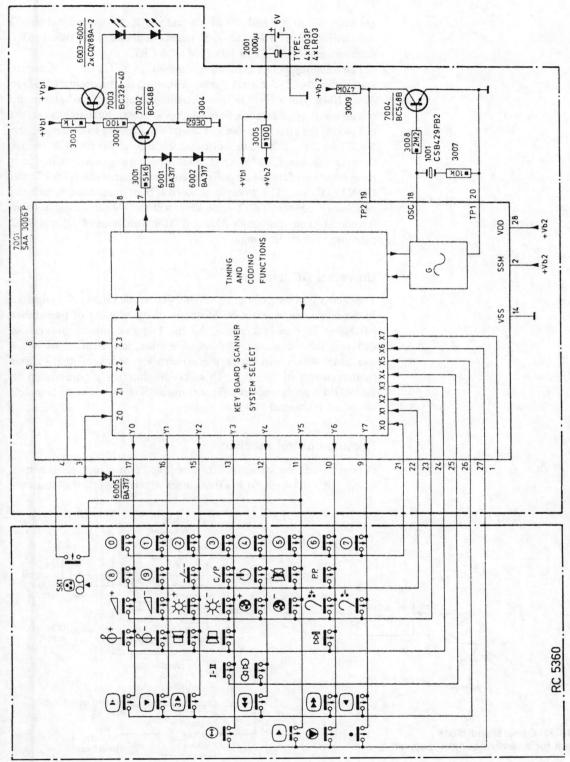

RC 5360

**Fig. 18.6** Infrared transmitter using a scanning encoder (Philips system 4)

encoder, X0 to X7 and Y0 to Y7 and the Z-Y matrix labelled Z0 to Z3 and Y0 to Y7. The Z-Y matrix together with switch SK1 determines the SYSTEM bits (TV of VCR).

The total number of possible commands is 64 for the X-Y matrix and 32 for the Z-Y matrix giving a theoretical maximum of 64 × 32 = 2048. However, far fewer commands are required and in the circuit under consideration only 49 keys are used. Scanning is carried out twice, the first time the Z-Y matrix is scanned to determine the SYSTEM bits of the data word and the second for the X-Y matrix to generate the COMMAND bits. The timing and coding unit completes the data word pulse stream by adding the START and CONTROL bits. The whole data word is then modulated by half the oscillator frequency (72/2 = 36 kHz) and this signal is used to drive the output stage, transistors 7002 and 7003 with diodes 6001 and 6002 providing signal limiting.

## Universal RC handset

The increase in the number of remotely controlled items of equipment in the home has meant a proliferation of the number of transmitter handsets. This is exacerbated by the fact that manufacturers use different RC techniques. To overcome this, universal handsets are available which can store the commands codes of the various manufacturers in memory. This may be done by programming an EEPROM with the required set of commands or by holding a complete set of all command codes in ROM.

## Remote control receiver

A generalised block diagram for a remote control receiver is shown in Fig. 18.7 in which D1 is a transducer which converts the ultrasonic

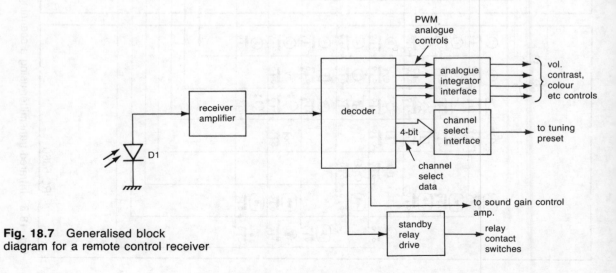

**Fig. 18.7** Generalised block diagram for a remote control receiver

or infrared waves into electrical signals. After amplification, the coded signal is fed into a decoder which translates the command word into a control output signal. Each output is fed into an appropriate interface circuit which carries out the control instruction.

### Analogue interface

When an analogue command is detected, the decoder produces a pulse-width modulated pulse train. The mark-to-space ratio of the pulse is used to change the setting of the control. With a high mark-to-space ratio, the mean d.c. level is high. This d.c. voltage is used to move the control in one direction. Conversely, when the mark-to-space ratio is low, the d.c. level is also low moving the control in the other direction. A typical interface circuit is shown in Fig. 18.8 in which R1/C1 is an integrator. Capacitor C1 charges up towards the mean d.c. voltage of the pulse-width modulated input, changing the base voltage of TR1 and with it the voltage across emitter resistor R2. This changed emitter voltage is then fed into the appropriate gain control amplifier to vary the setting of the selected control.

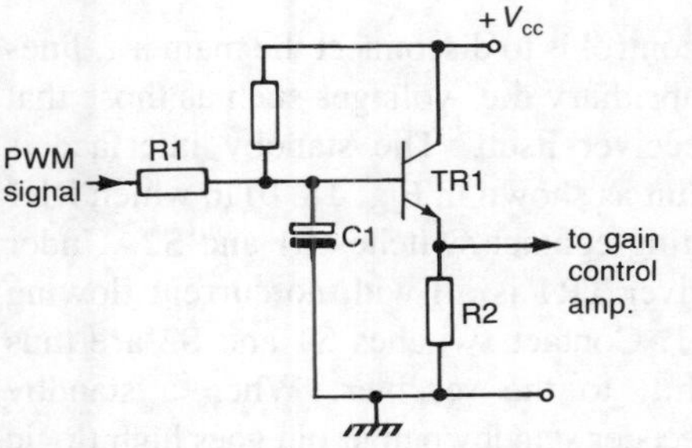

### Channel selection interface

Programme selection commands are translated into a four-bit parallel code data which provides $2^4 = 16$ different channel selections. The coded data are then fed into a 4-to-16 demultiplexer which activates

**Fig. 18.8** Interface circuit for analogue controls

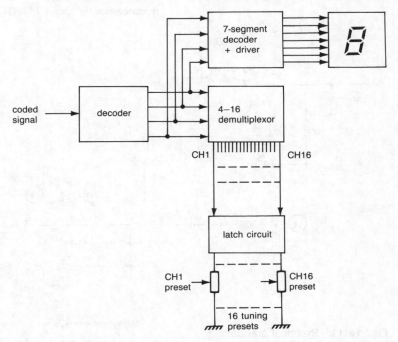

**Fig. 18.9** Channel selection interface

one and only one of its 16 outputs for each combination of the input data as shown in Fig. 18.9. The enabled output drives a latch which selects one of the 16 tuning presets. The four-bit data is also fed to a seven-segment decoder/driver to drive a seven-segment LED display.

## Standby interface

The purpose of the standby control is to disconnect the main h.t. lines from the receiver leaving subsidiary d.c. voltages such as those that feed the remote control receiver itself. The standby interface is essentially a relay drive circuit as shown in Fig. 18.10 in which RL1 is the relay armature operating contact switches S1 and S2. Under normal conditions, relay driver TR1 is off with no current flowing through relay armature RL1. Contact switches S1 and S2 are thus closed providing normal h.t. to the receiver. When a standby instruction is received, the decoder standby output pin goes high (logic 1) causing TR1 to conduct. TR1 current energises relay RL1 causing S1 and S2 to open, disconnecting h.t.1 and h.t.2 and turning the receiver off. Diode D1 is the normal protection diode which protects the relay driver transistor from any over-voltage resulting from the back e.m.f. induced in the relay armature when TR1 switches off.

A practical standby interface circuit is shown in Fig. 18.11 in which TS1 is the relay driver with D3 its protection diode, RE-1 is the relay armature and IC20 is the remote control decoding part of microcomputer chip UPD8049C. When a standby command has been

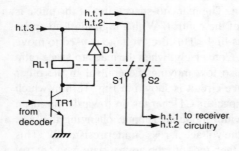

**Fig. 18.10**  Standby control interface

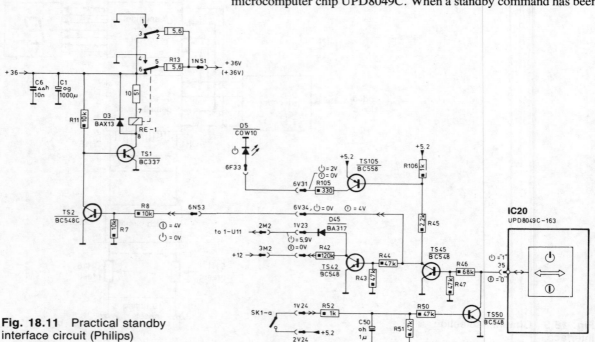

**Fig. 18.11**  Practical standby interface circuit (Philips)

received, pin 35 of IC20 switches from low to high, thus turning TS45 on. The low collector voltage of TS45 turns TS2 off and consequently TS1 on energising relay RE-1. Contacts 2 and 1, also 4 and 5 of the relay make, switching off the 36 V supply. The low voltage of TS45 collector also turns TS42 off so that D45 conducts via R42 which applies a high voltage (5.9 V) to pin 1 of main power supply unit U11 (not shown) switching off the main h.t. line. The circuit provides for a LED to indicate a standby mode. When the receiver is in the standby mode, with TS45 turned on, TS105 is turned on, driving current through LED indicator D5. When the receiver is switched on again pin 35 of IC20 goes from high to low. As a result T45 turns off, TS2 turns on, TS1 turns off and relay RE-1 is de-energised, Contacts 2 and 3, and contacts 5 and 6 make, restoring the 36 V supply. Furthermore, pin 1 of main power unit, U11, goes low enabling the h.t. supply and TS105 and D5 turn off.

### The decoder chip

A block diagram for an infrared remote control decoder chip is shown in Fig. 18.12. Remote control of the analogue settings (volume, brightness and colour) is achieved by digital-to-analogue conversion of the outputs of separate six-bit counters driven by clock pulses from

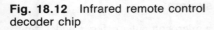

**Fig. 18.12** Infrared remote control decoder chip

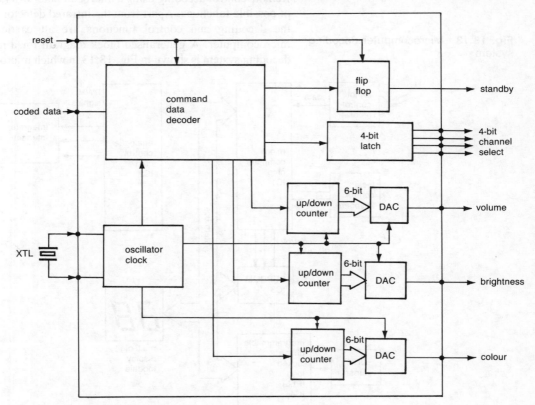

the oscillator. When an analogue up or down command is recognised by the decoder, the appropriate counter is incremented or decremented by the clock pulses as necessary. The counter's six-bit binary output is then converted into an analogue value by the digital-to-analogue converter. This analogue value is then used to control the pulse width of a square wave derived from the clock oscillator. A six-bit counter provides a maximum count of $2^6 = 64$. The analogue control voltage therefore varies in steps totalling 64. Given a command repetition frequency of say 100 ms, then it will take $64 \times 100\,\text{ms} = 6.4\,\text{s}$ to adjust the level from minimum to maximum or vice versa.

When a programme change command is received, the decoder converts the coded instruction into a four-bit binary number and stores it into a four-bit parallel latch. The decoder also determines the logic state of the standby output pin via the flip flop. When the receiver is in standby mode, the decoder sets the flip flop to produce a high and vice versa for normal operation. On switch on from the off or standby modes, a pulse is fed into the chip to reset the decoder and the standby for normal operation.

## Microcomputer decoding system

Remote control decoding using a microcomputer offers a wider range of possible functions. Apart from the infrared detector and amplifier, the decoding and control functions are all carried out by the microcomputer. A generalised block diagram for a microcomputer decoding system is shown in Fig. 18.13 in which microcomputer chip

**Fig. 18.13** Microcomputer decoding system

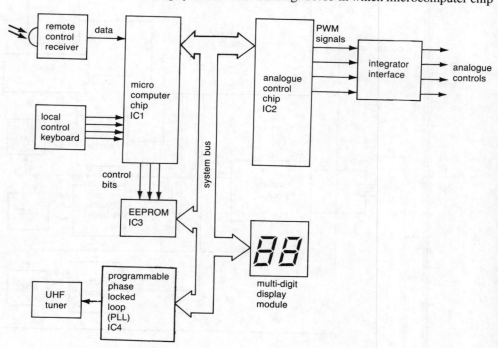

IC1 decodes commands from the remote control receiver as well as those from the local control keyboard matrix. The local control keyboard usually provides a number of functions including a synthesised tuning facility. The bus system allows the microcomputer chip IC1 to communicate with and control the other chips. IC1 sets the division ratio of the dividers within the programmable phase-locked loop, IC4 thus selecting the channel. The final tuning data is fed back to the microcomputer via the bus and stored into memory. The system ensures accurate tuning without the need for a.f.c. Any drift due to tuner ageing is compensated by the memory being continually refreshed. When the microcomputer detects an analogue control instruction, it sends the appropriate instruction to the analogue control chip IC2 via the bus. IC2 converts the instruction into a pulse-width modulated waveform which when integrated by the interface is used to vary the analogue setting. The system also provides for a multi-digit LED display controlled by the bus. Finally, memory chip IC3 stores all the relevant information with regard to the customer preferred analogue settings, channel frequencies and other settings at the manufacturing stage. The EEPROM is controlled by the microcomputer using a three-bit parallel code which instructs the chip to write, read, erase, etc.

We shall now describe the various parts of the computerised system.

## Receiver for microcomputer remote control systems

Apart from infrared detection by a transducer diode, the remote control receiver provides narrow band and selective amplification, demodulation and pulse shaping before feeding the data into the microcomputer. A practical circuit is shown in Fig. 18.14 in which IC1 provides the necessary pre-amplification after detection by D1. IC1 incorporates automatic gain control which ensures that TS3 receives a constant amplitude signal. The signal level is determined by the setting of preset R11. Demodulation is carried out by TS3,

**Fig. 18.14** Receiver for microcomputer remote control system (Philips)

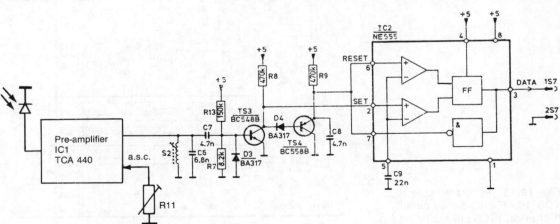

TS4 and IC2 which detects the envelope of the modulating 36 kHz frequency. TS3 is biased so that it conducts at the positive peaks of the 36 kHz modulating signal. The resulting negative-going pulses at the collector of TS3 drives the SET input of IC2 (pin 2) so that the signal on output pin 3 becomes high. Resetting occurs when the RESET input (pin 6) exceeds a certain trigger level. The RESET input is controlled by TS4. When a remote control signal is received, TS4 is turned on (via D4) by the negative-going voltage at the collector of TS3, keeping the RESET input below its threshold level. At the end of the 36 kHz burst, TS4 turns off allowing C8 to charge via R9 which raises the RESET input above the trigger level pulling pin 6 to zero. Pins 7 and 6 are also pulled to zero by the action of the NOT gate in IC2 discharging C8. The sequence is then repeated for the next burst of carrier frequency and so on to reproduce the original coded pulse stream.

## Programmable PLL chip

A circuit diagram of a programmable PLL chip TD6316 AP used by Ferguson is shown in Fig. 18.15. The chip is controlled by the central control unit via a three-line Thomson bus, data/clock/enable. An 18-bit data word is entered whenever the enable line (pin 2) is held high

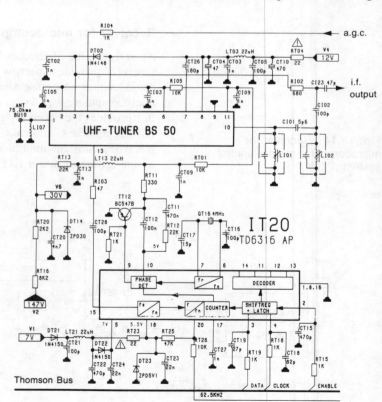

**Fig. 18.15** Programmable PLL TD6316 AP chip based circuit (Ferguson ICC5 chassis)

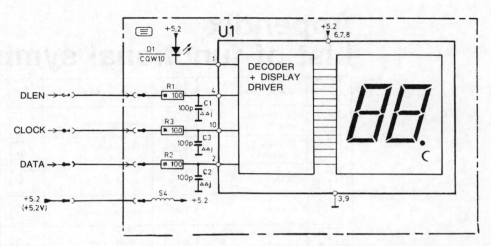

**Fig. 18.16** A two-digit bus controlled display module (Philips)

which occurs whenever there is a channel selection. The data bits are stored in the shift register latch and subsequently decoded to set the division ratio of programmable divider f/fn. The resulting frequency is then fed into the phase detector where it is compared with the constant frequency derived from a 4 MHz crystal. A factor of 512 is used to divide the 4 MHz signal to produce a very stable frequency of 4 MHz/512 = 7812.5 Hz. The output from the discriminator is used to control transistor TT12, which functions as a variable load resistor for the 30 V tuning voltage produced by diode DT14. A tuning voltage of 0.5 V to 30 V is thus made available to the tuner. Tuner frequency at pin 13 of the tuner is fed back to the frequency divider f/fn via prescaler fo/fn to complete the loop.

### LED display module

A circuit of a two-digit bus controlled display is shown in Fig. 18.16 with an additional LED which when illuminated appears as a 'decimal point' to indicate that a channel number is being displayed. There is a further LED, D1, which lights up when the teletext mode is selected. The decoder and display driver chip is controlled via a three-line DBUS system by the CCU. The data signal comprises 18 bits which includes information for the teletext LED and the 'decimal point', the first and last bits providing the address of the converter chip. The chip converts the binary coded programme or channel number sent along the DATA line into a seven-segment code to drive the two digits.

# Appendix
# List of functional symbols

| | | | | | |
|---|---|---|---|---|---|
| | Changer, general | | Band-stop filter | | Amplifier, general |
| | Interference separator | | Band-pass filter | | Stand-by |
| | Synchronisation separator | | Pulse-width modulator | | On/off |
| DIV | Divider | $\varphi_{90°}$ | 90° phase shifter | | Output stage |
| | Rectifier | | Electronic switch | | Controlled amplifier |
| | Automatic Gain Control | | Variable impedance | | Differential amplifier |
| F F H/2 | Flip-flop on half line frequency | | Display | | Amplifier with limiter |
| G | Square wave generator | ns | Delay element | | Positive peak clipper |
| G | Sawtooth generator | | Detector | | Black level restorer |
| G | Sinewave generator | | Phase detector | | Coaxial aerial input |
| G | Adjustable sinewave generator | | Voltage stabilizer | | RC network (integrator) |
| | Rejection filter | | FM detector | matrix | Decoding matrix |
| | Low-pass filter | | Phase discriminator | IR | Infra red transmitter |
| | High-pass filter | | Colour killer | IR | Infra red receiver |
| | Sound mute | | Search control | | Multi-function switch |
| VCR | VCR switch | | Band selection | PAL | Modulator |
| M | Mixer stage | | Constant level | $\nabla_{I/II}$ | Mono I or II sound |
| EF | Emitter follower | | Variable level | | Stereo sound |
| | Tuning control | | Input-control | | Spatial stereo |
| | A.F.C. function | | De-emphasis | | Schmitt trigger |
| | A.F.C. control | | Shaper | | Volume control |
| | General operating command | | AND gate | | Balance control |
| | Search function | ≥1 | OR gate | | Bass and treble control |

# Index